DOUBT AND CERTAINTY IN SCIENCE

A BIOLOGIST'S REFLECTIONS ON THE BRAIN

BY

J. Z. YOUNG

M.A., F.R.S.

PROFESSOR OF ANATOMY AT
UNIVERSITY COLLEGE, LONDON

The B.B.C. Reith Lectures
1950

OXFORD
AT THE CLARENDON PRESS
1951

Oxford University Press, Amen House, London E.C. 4

GLASGOW NEW YORK TORONTO MELBOURNE WELLINGTON
BOMBAY CALCUTTA MADRAS CAPE TOWN

Geoffrey Cumberlege, Publisher to the University

PRINTED IN GREAT BRITAIN

PREFACE

THE REITH LECTURES for 1950 are here printed as they were given, with only the alterations necessary to make reading reasonably smooth. In preparing the lectures I was aware that the information was often unduly concentrated and that it needed amplification. In order to provide this without interfering with the individual lectures themselves, I have therefore added five chapters of comment, placed between the lectures. I hope that by reading directly through the book, including these comments, the reader will get a complete view of the thesis.

After much deliberation I have decided not to add a comment to the last lecture. There is obviously very much that could be said to expand the attempt to forecast the effects upon society of these new ways of speaking. I am much tempted to do it, but am very conscious of the great dangers that face the biologist if he tries to turn sociologist, without prolonged study of the enormous and diffuse problems that are involved.

There is plenty of evidence that scientists make foolish statements when they try to speak or write for large numbers of people. I have been most painfully aware that my language has not always been effective or even consistent, and I fear that theologians and philosophers in particular will dismiss much of what I have to say as simple-minded, because it is not written in the usual idiom of their systems. However, scientific language changes year by year. Scientists believe that they must doubt even the apparently most fundamental laws. Is it possible that there are significant aspects of language that even philosophers have not yet discovered? The scientist would not be surprised to find that it was so. Indeed, he would be suspicious of anyone who claimed that the last and best word on *any* subject had already been said, by Plato or anyone else. Let us praise famous men and their works, by all means, but a still more important duty is to improve on what they have done. We can look back with pride at human achievements, but surely everyone looking at the difficulties that still face mankind must feel that we should try to improve even further on the system of communication provided for us by philosophers, theologians, and scientists.

The way of speaking used in these lectures is that of a biologist reared in the tradition of study of evolution, of anatomy, and of physiology. It would be impossible for me to trace out in a short space even the major writers who have influenced me in arriving at this position; the discerning eye will detect them soon enough. I have followed the tradition of empiricist philosophy, through A. N. Whitehead, to the modern British exponents, especially Ayer and Ryle. The application of such methods to psychology and the study of behaviour comes from William James, J. Loeb, J. B. Watson, and K. S. Lashley. If there is a special contribution in these lectures it is perhaps in allying these methods with those of the anatomist, physiologist, and evolutionary bio-logist. My sources here are the whole tradition of British Zoology, especially as expressed in the work of E. S. Good-rich and D'Arcy Thompson, who in their differing ways called attention to the study of living form. In recent years we have learned new ways of speaking about how living organization evolves, through the study of populations by J. B. S. Haldane, R. A. Fisher, and many others. L. Hogben has shown how such biological methods can be applied to a wide range of human affairs.

It would be impossible to mention a fair sample of the studies that make up even the background of our knowledge of the nervous system, around which the whole thesis of the lectures is built. Sir Charles Sherrington's contribution is evident throughout and a similarly pervasive influence is that of E. D. Adrian's studies of so many aspects of the electrical activities of the brain and nerves. It is not perhaps generally realized how greatly all such work depends on exact descrip-tion of the detailed structure of the cells of the brain, as was given by Ramon y Cajal, and of the network of tracts of fibres that connect the parts, to which W. E. Le Gros Clark has recently added so much.

Many new ideas are now being contributed to the study of the nervous system through the interest of mathematicians and engineers, such as A. S. Turing, and N. Wiener. I hope that the force of their contribution is felt in the text, though I have not been able to use their symbolism.

The quotation of sources for general scientific theory is an absurd as well as invidious business. Much is contributed by a few great initiators, but the body of scientific knowledge is made up of the vast mass of detail provided by many individual workers. It is this body of detailed knowledge, freely available, that makes science a valuable agent for use by all mankind.

I owe a very great deal to the stimulus I have received from interchanges with many colleagues in London and Oxford, some of whom were good enough to read part or all of the script. H. Dingle, A. J. Ayer, T. D. Weldon, D. Forde, E. A. Blake Pritchard, D. Sholl, F. Roberts, helped especially in this way. I often foolishly neglected their advice, but where I have taken it the text has become very much improved. I owe a special debt to Mr. Brian Boycott for his assistance with the experiments on the octopus—indeed it was he who performed nearly all of them. Much scientific work nowadays depends on skilled technical help, and I should like to thank the technical staff of the Department of Anatomy at University College for all they have done in this respect, and especially Mr. F. J. Pittock and Mr. J. Armstrong, for the beautiful microscopic preparations and photographs made under their direction. The scripts of some of the lectures ran through as many as six versions, and I am very grateful to Miss P. Codlin and Miss M. J. West for their patience over preparing these. Miss E. R. Turlington drew the line-drawings with her usual skill.

If the lectures were understandable when delivered it was mainly due to Mr. R. Lewin of the B.B.C. who advised me throughout. Had I taken his advice more often they would have been clearer still. The British Public is to be congratulated on having a Broadcasting Service that makes available such intelligent, competent, and patient production work to assist its speakers.

J. Z. Y.

June 1951

CONTENTS

LIST OF ILLUSTRATIONS

First Lecture

THE BIOLOGIST'S APPROACH TO MAN

WHEN I was asked whether I would consider undertaking the Reith Lectures, I said that it might be possible to give some idea of the methods of science by describing the various sorts of work at present in progress on the brain. Frankly I did not consider that this would be a piece of research. The scientist does not usually think of the writing of books or preparing of lectures as research. Writing seems to him to be a rather tiresome labour that he must do after the fun of laboratory research and discovery is over. I therefore sat down to use the time available more in hope of making a summary than a discovery. But when I began to do this I came to realize the extent to which having to describe the results of one's thoughts to others is a part of the process of discovery itself. We are social creatures, depending far more than we realize on communication with each other. We can understand better both the workings of the brain and the nature of scientific inquiry itself if we realize how deeply our whole life is influenced by this necessity of communication. Paying attention to this fact has made me think in a way that is new and helpful to me, and I hope may be so for others also.

One of the characteristics of scientists and their work, curiously enough, is a certain confusion, almost a muddle. This may seem strange if you have come to think of science with a big S as being all clearness and light. There is indeed a most important sense in which science stands for law and certainty. Scientific laws are the basis of the staggering achievements of technology that have changed the Western world, making it, in spite of all its dangers, a more comfortable and a happier place. But if you talk to a scientist you may soon find that his ideas are not all well ordered. He loves discussion, but he does not think always with complete, consistent schemes, such as are used by philosophers, lawyers, or clergymen. Moreover, in his laboratory he does not spend much of his time thinking about scientific laws at all. He is busy with other things, trying to get some piece of apparatus to work, finding a way of measuring something more exactly, or making dissections that will show the parts of an animal or plant more clearly. You may feel that he hardly knows himself what law he is trying to prove. He is continually observing, but his work is a feeling out into the dark, as it were. When pressed to say what he is doing he may present a picture of uncertainty or doubt, even of actual confusion.

This mixture of doubting with the certainty of scientific laws is not a new phenomenon. We had a chance recently to see it stretching over three whole centuries in the celebrations of the third centenary of Newton's birth in 1642. The Royal Society asked a number of learned men to write about Newton. Some placed great emphasis on the fact that Newton would not speculate 'beyond the limits where quantitative confirmation could be sought from nature'. They quoted Newton's famous remark, '*hypotheses non fingo*'—'I do not make hypotheses'. By this he meant that he only derived laws from observations of nature, a process that he considered to be distinct from framing an hypothesis as to the causes of the phenomena. Those who are attracted by this side of Newton's character emphasize his constant work in the laboratory, how he made his own mirrors, his own experiments with light, and endless other matters. He was one of the most exact, practical, and knowledgeable persons who has ever lived. 'I do not deal in conjectures', he himself said. Evidently for some people this is the typical picture of a scientist. But wait a minute. When Newton said that he did not deal in conjectures he was eighty-one years old. Other learned men investigating his writings have proved that what he said about himself was not true. He *did* make hypotheses and conjectures; from his young and most fruitful period onwards he made them endlessly. Some of them were very good hypotheses—Newton developed a general theory that matter is made of atoms. We can hardly make a better one today. But he could not prove it; he could neither see the atoms nor detect the forces that bind them together, as we can do now. His theory was therefore a sort of guess —a conjecture. He made another guess about an aether that pervades all space. And he puzzled over much more curious matters than these. He spent a great deal of time studying the writings of mystics, theologians, and alchemists. For weeks on end he worked in his laboratory making experiments to find the philosophers' stone that would turn lead into gold. He left a mass of writing on these magical and alchemical subjects, writings so diffuse that they have never been published. The late Lord Keynes, commenting on these papers, suggested that Newton was not so much one of the first men of the age of reason as the last of the magicians. He seems to have thought of the universe as a riddle posed by God, which could be solved if one looked hard enough for the clues. Some of the clues were to be sought in nature, others had been revealed in sacred and occult writings. The search for the answers was a continual struggle and anxiety, and it drove Newton to the edge of madness.

The point for us is that Newton did not spend his time simply observing nature. Besides doing that his brain also tried to put all the observations together, to fit them into general schemes. This search is the process that I call doubting. It is a process of exploration, and when significant resemblances are found we say that a new law has been promulgated, that some degree of certainty has been achieved.

What I hope to be able to demonstrate is that this mixture of doubt and certainty is not at all an accident. It is the very nature and essence of scientific method. Moreover, it is not by any means a character peculiar to science. Science is only the latest product of the human brain, which has been working in essentially the same way for the last 10,000 years: that is to say for the period of our history as a social animal.

Still the matter does not end there. This method of proceeding is but a development of the way in which all brains work. Indeed, I shall try to show that there is something corresponding to the discovery of certainty through doubt in all the operations of living things.

This is a formidable task, and I became conscious as I proceeded of how much one needs to know of history, psychology, anthropology, mathematics, and many other things. But to be able to see in perspective the range of phenomena from the nature of human thinking and scientific inquiry to the facts of evolution (and perhaps even of cosmology) would be such a clarification that it is worth the attempt. I feel that I have made some progress in this direction, and cannot do less than ask you to share the results, taking what may be wrong with anything that is right.

The method I have followed is simple enough. I have looked at man as a modern biologist looks at plants and animals. How do biologists work and what language do they use to describe their view of the world? We might say that they examine how each sort of animal and plant manages to keep its kind alive. Every creature maintains its organization distinct from the surroundings: it prevents itself from returning to dust. Biologists study how even the humblest plant is a wonderfully organized system of roots, stem, leaves, and flowers arranged to do this. These parts all act together to extract from the simple materials of soil and air the means to build the plant and propagate its kind. In animals, similarly, the various parts act together to nourish and protect the organization and enable it to continue.

The biologists' question about man is, therefore, how does he get his living on the earth? What are the means by which the continuity of human life is ensured? In answering it some biologists might say: 'Man is an omnivorous, terrestrial, bipedal mammal', or some such talk. I believe that such phrases show where we biologists have all been wrong. We have been concentrating on those features of man that

are obviously like those of animals; his digestion, his loco-
motion, and so on. We have been very much more loath to
realize that we can apply the same methods also to his higher
functions. Eating and walking are not the really important
features of man. We all recognize that it is far more significant that he is, shall we say, a thinking creature, or a worshipping one. What we have not sufficiently considered is
that it is just these traits of what we commonly call man's
mind that are also his most peculiar and important *biological*
characteristics. These are the features by which he gets his
living: they are the very ones that should most attract our
attention as biologists.

Each animal has some special ways of conducting its life.
The cow and sheep have special stomachs that digest grass.
The tiger has its teeth, the elephant its trunk and its teeth,
and so on. What then are the special characteristics of modern
man? Surely the chief one is that of co-operation between
individuals. Man's large brain is used to develop an intricate
social system, based mainly on communication by words.
Man has many other special features, such as good eyes for
getting information, and good hands for doing intricate
things. But it is chiefly co-operation that enables him to
obtain a living for more than 2,000,000,000 human beings
scattered over nearly all regions of the earth. Sophocles
expressed it long ago in a few words when he said: 'Of all
the wonders none is more wonderful than man—who has
learned the arts of speech, of windswift thought, and of
living in neighbourliness.' These are indeed the matters that
must chiefly engage the serious student of man. Of course on
this subject of human co-operation a vast mass of knowledge
has been collected by generations of anthropologists, psychologists, sociologists, and others. But there is, even yet, no
coherent body of knowledge about the biology of man that
sets him in his proper place in the living world. Biologists are
only now beginning to study what may be called the higher
attributes of man, his language, his social behaviour, his
religion, and his science. We may find valuable new ideas by

applying the biological method to the very highest of our activities and correlating these with the study of the organ that mediates them—the brain.

The factor we have been ignoring is that these special features of man are all due to the fact that he has developed far beyond other animals in the power of communication between individuals. Biologists have so far neglected to give full attention to the significance of communication in our species. The subject has been forced on their attention in recent years by the great development of mechanical aids to communication. There has already been some useful co-operation between biologists studying the brain and the engineers and mathematicians responsible for radio, television, and similar new devices. One result has been the comparison of the brain with calculating machines, but that is really only a detail. What is much more important is that we are now beginning to understand the importance of communication itself as a human activity. By thinking about this we shall find, I believe, a remarkable clarification of our ideas. What I hope to show is that proper use of communication has been the chief secret of the success of human societies in the past, and that it will certainly be so in both the immediate and the more distant future. Evidence of this is the fact that very extensive parts of the brain are concerned with speech. We are only beginning to understand, however, how the brain works to produce particular methods of speaking. Societies certainly change their methods of communication through the centuries. Recently the Western world has developed a whole set of new techniques for the transfer of information. As a result, co-operation between individuals has improved, and better and better tools and machines have been produced. Men have gradually learned the great advantages that come from being able to convey information fully and exactly to each other. The impact of new techniques of communication is felt in all sorts of ways. Everyone appreciates that the spread of education transforms society. When allied to science it gives great new powers to a community. It is perhaps not too much to say that we owe our survival to the radar communicating devices that helped to win the Battle of Britain. Modern armies, by making use of their well-trained brains and new equipment, can overwhelm less developed organizations. These are particular examples of the power that comes from good communication.

But much more important in the long run are the ways in which large groups of people are knit together. It is only by proper communication that human societies retain the adherence of their members. Perhaps nothing is more important for our future than to discover the best ways of obtaining knowledge about these matters. We are apt to use it at present for the interest of particular groups, classes, or countries. These are indeed natural units of communication and it would be unrealistic to ignore their importance. But we can try to find ways of making as many as possible of them interact for the benefit of mankind as a whole. Whether we like it or not, we can be sure that societies that use to the full the new techniques of communication, by better language and by better machines, will eventually replace those that do not.

What I am going to discuss, therefore, is how the brain makes communication between human beings possible. Here we come against a difficulty that is bound to worry us a lot. We seem to have two ways of talking about these matters. On the one hand each of us knows that he or she has what seem to be their private experiences, sensations, thoughts, pleasures, and pains. These are, in some sense, for each of us our own. They seem to occur in us, and yet are not part of our physical body. On the other hand, when we talk about communication we are also obviously discussing what we call a physical system; there is a transmitter (the brain, tongue, and larynx) in one person and a receiving system (the ears and brain) in the other. This is the famous dualism of mind and matter, which is perhaps the central problem of modern philosophy, religion, and science. No doubt most of us have felt the block to our thinking imposed by the obscurity of the relation of mind and matter. The consideration of this problem by philosophers in recent years has shown how easily we are deceived in the way we use such words as 'mind'. I propose to try to show how we can perceive one main source of these confusions. We may perhaps even devise a way of speaking that avoids the dilemma altogether.

Consider first that without leaving the topic of the brain we can at least begin to discuss many, perhaps all, human activities. The method that I am going to suggest as a working basis is to organize *all* our talk about human powers and capacities around knowledge of what the brain does. When the philosopher studies the way in which people think, let him consider what activity this represents in the brain: for certainly there is some. When the theologian studies the fact that human beings tend to organize their activities around statements about gods, let him consider the activity that this involves in the brain. When the educationist and psychologist follow the ways in which the child grows to his mature powers and later perhaps goes astray, let them consider the processes of the development and decay of the activities of the brain.

This is a very simple, straightforward way of proceeding and yet it may seem strange and new. People are curiously unwilling to accept and use the simple and obvious idea that all the things that they do, including the more complicated ones (say, painting a picture), involve activity in their brains. Indeed you may deny what I have just said. 'But it's not true that my brain paints the picture—it is *I* who do that. I am not just a mass of whitish stuff inside my skull.' But at least you will agree that in painting a picture the eye is receiving light and sending messages to the brain. Then, after appropriate activity, the brain sends other messages back to the hands. 'Yes,' you may reply, 'I agree about that, but what about thinking, when it is *all* internal?' There, too, I am prepared to say that there are some brain processes at work whenever anyone thinks. Moreover, I propose to show that it is not impossible that these could be detected. Then I could literally read your thoughts. 'An unpleasant prospect,' you might reply, 'but in any case where is all this getting us? What about my pains and pleasures, hopes and fears, all my experience? They still remain mine, don't they? However much I share them with you that does not alter the fact that there is an I experiencing them, who am in some way distinct from my body. Surely this experience is for me the ultimate reality.'

I agree that there is a sense in which we can say that this is so. But it is important to realize how extraordinarily difficult it is going to be to find that sense. As the biologist sees it, our brains are so constituted that we have learned to speak always in terms of self and otherness. From babyhood onwards we learn to satisfy our needs by communicating with others and eliciting their co-operation. Our brains therefore come to act in ways that are effective for this purpose. We soon acquire, for instance, the habit of focusing attention on certain sorts of objects around us and naming them. The brain has remarkable powers of comparing each new object with some familiar one, and this tendency can be seen at work in the growth of the habit of speaking of I, of oneself, the habit that gives rise to so much of the confusion over mind and body. In order to speak about ourselves we use the convention that placed in some way within us there is an agent who is said to act as we describe other men acting. This habit of postulating active creatures within bodies, the habit of animism, is an extremely convenient device for communication. It enables us to speak of the actions of all sorts of things in terms of the actions of people, which are easily described, and this has become an integral part of our Western system of communication. We do not find it easy to talk without speaking of some entity, the self, communicating with others. Our brains have become so arranged that we organize nearly all our experience into these forms in order to talk about it. We can say if we like that our experience is our own; but we are so built that we must try to communicate it. To do this we put this so-called raw experience into the form that there is something called 'me' here, communicating with a something 'not me'.

I do not propose to pursue the question farther here, philosophers can do it far better than I can. It seemed to me to be essential to raise it in the very first lecture, difficult though it may be to grasp. I am going to ask you to consider all our highest thoughts and aspirations as functions of the brain. This would seem absurd if I did not make it clear that for each of us, in some sense, what we call our inner experience is the central fact. I hope that it will gradually appear how this central fact of living becomes in modern man translated, as it were, to reveal what we agree to call a world outside ourselves. The world is like that for us because we put as much as possible of our experience into a form suitable for communication to others. I shall try to show how it comes about that we speak of ourselves as distinct entities, set in our bodies, able to communicate with others like ourselves. I shall try to show how our brains make us able to communicate by comparing one thing with another. In early stages of human communication man described the action of all bodies as caused by spirits or powers resident within them. Recently we have learned that it is better not to use this animistic way of speaking about physical things. Perhaps therefore we do not even need to do it when talking about ourselves, or each other. We may be able ultimately to dispense with the concept of mind altogether.

Science has discovered that it can do without animistic models. Instead it speaks about whatever part of the world it is studying by comparison with man-made machines. Further, science has developed all sorts of other special techniques of communication, such as mathematics. It will be the aim of these lectures to try to show how the brain works, using these new models. I shall discuss their advantages and their limitations. Certainly we have considerably improved our ways of speaking in recent years, so that we come to talk in greater and greater detail about phenomena and hence to control them better. Such improvement has been going on by fits and starts ever since the beginning of human history. We shall be able to follow how man has improved in this respect. He has gradually given up speaking about almost all aspects of the world as consisting of entities that are moved by capricious spirits. He has reached a state where all men can agree about the occurrence of many marvellous phenomena, which were previously not understood, or even were wholly unknown. But we remain men and not supermen: we must use the natures and habits that we inherit, including those of language. Let us then try to see what the biologist can tell us about man.

This will mean spending some time describing what has been found out about nerves and the brain. We speak about such matters, as about most other things, mainly by comparison. I shall do this in the case of the brain, discussing, for instance, in what ways it is like a calculating machine. This procedure of finding analogies is a characteristic human method. It suggests, as we shall often see, new ways of looking, which actually lead us to new discoveries. The brain is continually searching for fresh information about the rhythm and regularity of what goes on around us. This is the process that I call doubting, seeking for significant new resemblances. Once they are found they provide us with our system of law, of certainty. We decide that this is what the world is like and proceed to talk about it in those terms. Then sooner or later someone comes along who doubts, someone who tries to make a new comparison; when he is successful, mankind learns to communicate better and to see more.

So I shall have much to say about how the brain makes comparisons. We shall find that its mode of doing so is continually modified by the happenings that occur to it. This is the process that we call learning. I shall discuss what little is known of the actual changes that learning involves in the brain, and follow how the child learns its system of certainty, its laws of acting, by the process of a series of operations of doubt. After that I shall try to trace how human society has developed its plan of brain action, which is handed on from generation to generation, and shall give examples of how the earliest systems of brain action were modified to produce those current in the Middle Ages. These in turn gave rise by gradual development to the ways of acting that we call scientific. Finally, I shall discuss how earlier scientific ways have themselves become modified and enlarged, by a continuation of the same process.

But of course it is no good hoping to learn to understand all the functions of the brain in a series of eight lectures. You would not expect me in this time to teach you how to analyse and make a wireless set, or even how to drive a railway engine. The human brain is enormously more complicated than such machines. To understand it we shall need a collection of specialists at least as numerous as our present engineers and we shall have to learn to use words that are at least as obscure as theirs. At present there are relatively few people at work on the subject of the brain and little is known. Of course the reason for that is not just short-sightedness; it is literally that the study of the human brain has seemed so difficult that few have liked to attempt it. Not many people have been able to see even that there could be wide and powerful generalizations made about the brain, still less that there could be practical applications of this knowledge.

Such short-sightedness is not a new phenomenon. In much the same way there were only a few people in the Middle Ages who could see that it was worth while to study physical science or astronomy. When they did begin to do so they found that it showed them how to navigate and to do all sorts of practical things. Man has been gradually learning the possibility of using new techniques of communication ever since his earliest days. The information we have collected about the brain is now at last sufficient to be of some use to us. We are beginning already to see the sources of some of our more crude brain disorders. Surgeons can some-times help us to overcome epilepsy and a few of the difficul-ties of communication that twenty years ago would have been called purely 'mental'. Two hundred years ago these same conditions would have led to suspicion of possession by evil spirits, perhaps even to execution for witchcraft. But even more fundamental than these practical medical applications of knowledge about the brain is the advantage of the greatly increased understanding it gives us about ourselves. I hope that I shall be able in this way to show you that by further study of these matters we may see the connexion between our doubts, longings, and highest aspirations and the pro-cesses that have been going on in animals for hundreds of millions of years, perhaps with the eternal processes of the stars. These are high aims; but would you expect less from the study of man's unique feature, his brain?

Comment on the First Lecture

THE method suggested in these lectures is a combination of the techniques of evolutionary biologists and communication engineers. It may make the method clearer to add here some further details about how this combination has grown up. In every age men speak about themselves and the world around them partly by making comparison with the tools that they use. Conversely, they describe the actions of their tools by speaking of them as if they were men. Some of the most powerful of our modern tools are those used for communication, the telegraph, telephone, and especially radio; therefore in recent years biologists have begun to use the language of the communication engineer to describe the behaviour of animals and men. This language has been especially useful for those who study the brain, whose functions, in man, are largely concerned with establishing communication between individuals.

Some of the best mathematical brains have recently been devoted to analysis of the processes of control and regulation of machines and the communication of information. They have worked out what system of signs or coding enables us to convey the greatest possible amount of information in a given time by telegraph, radio, or other means. Dr. N. Wiener has been especially prominent in this work and he has attempted to make its results available in his book on what he calls Cybernetics—the study of governors or steerers. Being a mathematician, however, his explanation uses a symbolism that can only be properly understood by those whose knowledge of mathematics is considerable. It may be argued that this is inevitable since the ways that engineers use for speaking about these subjects are largely mathematical and that it is therefore absurd and illogical to bowdlerize them by turning them into ordinary speech. Undoubtedly mathematics provides a powerful means of saying things exactly and briefly. Being myself a feeble mathematician I am in no position to say whether the ideas of these engineers lose all value without their symbolism. However, I have found that emphasis on the significance of communication certainly seems to help a great deal in clearing up even the most persistent difficulties that arise in common speech, for example the meanings that we attach to the words 'mind' and 'matter'. The Reith Lectures provided a good opportunity to test whether these ways of speaking are useful also for others. The lectures have been established as a tribute to Lord Reith's pioneer work in developing a new form of communication. It is appropriate that this tribute should take the form of giving to many people lectures more difficult than they are accustomed to follow, and it is particularly suitable that they should be devoted to exploring some of the wider implications of the extension of communication that Reith has done so much to foster.

There is a continual alternation in the use of words for describing man's own actions and those of the tools that he produces. Men first spoke of fire as a living thing, then having discovered a use for it and invented cooking, people went on to speak of vital fires and vital cookings within them. So in the development of modern science physicists and engineers first spoke of the tools that they made as using 'force' and doing 'work', as a human body was said to do. Then, after such terms had been made exact and a mathematical language had been developed for describing events in terms of them, biology was able to borrow them back again. The novel tools of the nineteenth and early twentieth centuries were power tools, steam and gas engines and dynamos. Correspondingly the physiology of that time dealt mainly with the interchanges of work and energy in the body. It investigated how much fuel the body needs, and how much oxygen to burn it. There was elaborate analysis of the efficiency with which the muscles work, how much heat they produce, and so on. This knowledge is the classical framework of physiology, based on classical physics and engineering. It uses as its language Newton's dynamics, which assumes that we begin with a system of particles whose state is known and then discover what happens when they are acted upon by known forces.

The early developments of electrical engineering followed this same classical scheme in that they were also concerned with power. More recently, however, there has developed a whole new branch of the subject, sometimes called small current engineering. This is concerned with using electrical effects not to do the heavy work for man but to control the machines which do that work and to improve communication between people. These functions of control and communication had originally been performed by man alone. In developing ways of talking about the new machines the small current engineers therefore borrowed the terms that were previously used to describe human communication, just as their predecessors had borrowed the terms energy, force, and work which describe human effort. Engineers and laboratory workers very readily borrow terms in this way and use them first as a kind of slang among themselves. The study of the development of language in workshops would be a very rewarding one. It is important that when such laboratory slang is found to be more widely useful its origins should be recognized and its new content defined as accurately as possible.

The communication engineer talks a great deal about 'information', a term originally used in an entirely human context to indicate what one person tells another. It is important to be clear what this term comes to mean to the biologist, who studies the behaviour of organisms. He sees every organism as a system continually interchanging with its environment. Every race of plant, animal, or man maintains its organization by taking in food, water, and oxygen. With the energy provided by these it does work of various sorts to keep itself intact. In order that the body shall do the right things to achieve this end it must receive 'information' about the changes that go on in the world around it, and indeed also in the different parts of its own body. It is the function of the sense organs, or as they are better called receptors, to provide this information. Any system, say the body, is said to be able to receive information if when a change occurs the system is capable of reacting in such a way as to maintain its own stability. Raindrops falling cannot be said to carry information, but raindrops falling on a person's head inform him how hard it is raining. To speak of a change as giving information implies that there is somewhere a receiver able to react appropriately to the change.

Engineers have produced many machines that are able to receive and react to information and to exert control, for example by ensuring that some action continues in a steady way. A regulating machine of this sort is said to receive an input of information, from which, after calculation, it produces an output that exerts the control. The output may act in various ways—for instance by pulling upon wires or chains in the case of automatic steering devices. Especial use has been made of machines that are able to keep a vessel on a fixed course and comparison with these is valuable for biology because living things regulate in a similar way, in the sense that they maintain a steady state and tend to produce actions that correct any deviation from this state. The essential feature of steering machines that keep on a fixed course is known in the engineer's jargon as 'feed-back'. Every deviation of the rudder from the course is noted by a suitably sensitive receiving apparatus; this sends information that tends to correct the deviation. Much attention has been devoted to the theory of the way in which such devices can best be made to function to maintain stability. For example, if there is too strong a feed-back and any divergence is too powerfully corrected, there will be an overswing to the opposite direction and the system will then not maintain a steady course but will oscillate or zigzag.

Evidently these steering machines work very much like living things and we can recognize a great number of feed-back systems in the body. Information provided by each of the receptors tends to produce an action by the body that is appropriate to keep our life system stable in the light of the change that the receptor reports. We draw our hand away when the receptors record a high temperature; when our taste receptors record sweetness we swallow, and so on for all the other receptor systems, though some of the actions are very complicated. It should be possible to use the precise language developed by the engineers to improve our understanding of these feed-back systems that produce the stability of our lives. It cannot be said that physiologists have been able to go very far yet with this method. The living organism is so complicated that we seldom have enough data to be able to work out exactly what is happening by means of the mathematics that the engineer uses. Up to the present the general ideas and terminology used by these engineers have been of more value to biologists than have the detailed application of their techniques.

One of the chief methods of control that modern man uses to ensure his stability is his communication with others. This forms the basis of co-operative social action. The process of communication consists in converting the input of information that an individual receives into an output that also has the character of information, because it is directed to another person. This is only a roundabout way of saying that people talk, but speaking in this way with the combined language of the engineer and the biologist helps to make very much clearer the nature of all speech and writing. It emphasizes that these are but part of the system of control by which the stability of human organization is maintained. This should be obvious enough, but I hope that the lectures make clear how often we forget it and what a great increase of clarity results from emphasizing the fact that our words have biological functions.

The information that we convey to other people has the function of helping to ensure survival of ourselves or our race. It is therefore an output designed to have some regulating effect. The full sequence of communication involves sending of information from one individual to another, who then sends back a recognized or expected result, which helps to satisfy the need of the original sender. The exchange of information thus becomes reciprocal and the two or more people concerned form a co-operating system, whose final output is the tools, building operations, or the like that ensure the survival of the race.

In its usually accepted sense, therefore, the word communication implies interchange of information between two or more people or animals. We cannot speak of communication between two clouds, because their effects on each other are not interchanges between two self-regulating systems. Certain useful extensions of the use of the word communication arise, however, in relation to some of our own products, especially machines and some social organizations that are self-regulating. From speaking about these products we gain words that we use to describe each other. Many examples of this are given throughout these lectures; in the seventeenth century man was compared with a clock, in the twentieth with a calculating machine. Again, I suggest in the seventh lecture that there are some advantages in speaking of a person by comparison with the larger social organizations, which are also human products. There is, therefore, a sense in which we can say that there is communication of information between man and his products.

Human society has long been a self-regulating system and we can say that it preserves itself by conveying information to its members and receiving information from them. Human tools are also self-regulating, in so far as they convey to us sufficient power or information to ensure that we return to them the power and information needed for their continuance. This is the relationship, for example, between a man and his watch. Many people have feared that as our tools become more complicated they will control us instead of the other way round. There is indeed a sense in which as they become more fully self-regulating they become more independent and more able to tell us things that are useful. It is perhaps natural for each generation to fear its products, but surely it is more satisfactory to welcome their independence and the new information that they provide as an aid to the continuation of the whole system.

Through these lectures I have tried to trace the way in which change in communication systems has been a central feature of the changes that have come over human societies. The change is not steadily in the direction of increasing transfer of information, but the biologist and historian alike must recognize that the whole organization of our system today involves very much more detailed inter-communication than there was, say, 10,000 years ago. Moreover, there has been an accelerating change in this direction during the last three hundred years, following the adoption of a new system after the Middle Ages, and especially with the rise of science. Quite recent years have seen further great advances, not only in mechanical aids to communication, but also in the relationship between individuals. Comparison with the new tools, such as the radio, is bound to produce further big changes in the way we talk about ourselves. The rise of classical physics after the seventeenth century produced the habit of speaking about ourselves as machines, having 'structure' and 'functions.' This has allowed enormous improvement in the control of ourselves through medical science. But classical physics dealt mainly with the *work* that men and machines do and paid little attention to their *organization*. The new physics and engineering differ from the old in that they deal with complicated organizations and the way that they change. When we have learned to speak of our own organization in these terms our methods of controlling it should become much better, just as, by speaking of the body as a power machine, medicine has given us far greater control than did the animism and astrology of the Middle Ages. The method of classical physics is to postulate a system whose behaviour is completely known and whose future can therefore be determined. Physics has recently discovered that the complicated patterns of relationship between ourselves and what we observe cannot be described in this way. We have to start with an initial organization that we can describe only imperfectly and whose future we cannot forecast exactly. We can, however, determine the probability that it will behave in any given way. The new sort of physics is therefore said to be statistical and it employs a type of mathematics suitable for forecasting probabilities.

This development of methods for describing complicated organizations and forecasting their future brings the techniques of physics closer to those of biology. The biologist also cannot yet control exactly the conditions of the system he observes, because he cannot reproduce its past history. He has therefore developed statistical methods for forecasting as nearly as he can what organisms will do. These methods are related to those of the statistical physicist and the two sciences converge most closely in the study of communication, where neither can do without the other. The two techniques together provide us with a language in which we are gradually coming to speak in new ways about ourselves. With it we find that we can avoid some of the puzzles and obscurities that have arisen by the use of words based on the older comparisons. Throughout the lectures the inadequacy of many of our familiar words becomes apparent. I try to show that we can do better than by speaking of 'I myself', of 'my mind', 'soul', 'consciousness', 'knowledge', 'will', and many other such terms. Similarly in speaking about our surroundings the physicist no longer speaks of a 'world' of 'matter' or of 'force'. Finally there is not much sense any more in speaking of beginnings and endings, or of 'creation'.

All this may seem disturbing to many people; others will give the verdict that it is unnecessary and even silly. We need not be dogmatic or expect sudden changes of practice —but changes are certainly going on, as they always do. Probably we could not stop them. The discovery of new tools and new language is altering society, and in the last lecture I try to trace some of the directions of these alterations. There is no need to be unduly alarmed about them. Probably they will be fundamentally less radical than they may seem in prospect.

Those who are not accustomed to the language of behaviourism are apt to consider that it is in some way derogatory of human status and values. Certainly the behaviourist refuses to conduct all his descriptions with reference only to man; he tries to make comparision between man and other aspects of nature, and he holds that this increases rather than decreases our range of vision and hence our dignity. A more serious difficulty is the suspicion that in refusing to use such words as 'mind', 'will', and 'pleasure', the behaviourist wishes to take away altogether the experiences associated with these names and to 'reduce man to a mere machine'. To make any such attempt would of course be ludicrous— we all have the 'experience' of living. The behaviourist is particularly anxious that we should enlarge the scope of our lives. He believes that we can do this best by comparison of human life with that of other animals and with other natural phenomena. In particular he believes that we shall gain, not lose, by close investigation of the words that we use. Such investigation should specially pursue the problem of what we mean by speaking of our 'experience' and the nature of the entity we call our 'life'. The method insists that we should approach these problems as we should others in semantics. For example, when we say that the centre of life is the soul, we should ask exactly what observation it is that we wish to convey to each other. Doing this might lead us to alter our use of the word 'soul', perhaps even to abandon it. But this would only be because we believed that it was possible in some other way to convey *more* than the old word covers. The whole purpose of new words and comparisons is to *enlarge* our experience, not to reduce it.

Behaviourist language is often labelled as 'materialist'. If a materialist is a person unwilling to talk about indescribable entities, the behaviourist would be proud to accept the label. It is also true that he believes that we shall gain rather than lose by comparing man with 'material' objects. But this does not mean asserting that we know all about 'matter' and have nothing further to learn about the universe. The scientist is in a better position than anyone else to see that we are set about with mysteries. It is his business to grapple with ghosts every day of his life and he must refuse to allow them to be laid by the process of labelling them with a primitive nomenclature. The mysteries of the universe are too great to be expressed by such simple comparisons as are implicit in either the words 'spirit' or 'matter'.

On the other hand, the scientist agrees with other sensible men that our system of words must use some conventions if it is to be useful and ensure stability. Throughout these lectures I am feeling the way towards definition of a sure basis for such convention.

The biologist has the advantage of looking at millions of organisms spread over millions of years. He sees two things most clearly: first that each particular individual or type of organization seldom survives for very long. Nevertheless, he sees that living organization is one of the most stable things upon the earth: it changes, but only slowly: its continuity is the best reference point that we can see.

Second Lecture

BRAINS AS MACHINES

I HAVE already suggested that it would be possible to conduct our affairs somewhat better if we gave more consideration to the processes in the brain that accompany speech and thought. We have a great deal of information about these matters that was not available fifty or even ten years ago, but it would be misleading to suggest that we can yet provide a complete picture of brain action. Recent discoveries have shown enough, however, to give us hints as to how much we could do if we knew rather more. This lecture is an attempt to give an introduction to the ideas that scientists use to describe these discoveries about nerves and brains.

In the seventeenth century people began to make comparison of living things with the machines that were then being perfected. The French philosopher Descartes compared the body with a clock. In a clock one describes each of the parts as having a function in the working of the whole. This led Descartes to an idea that was quite novel at the time, namely that one could proceed to find out how all the parts of the body interact, investigating it as if it were a machine. Comparison of living things with machines may seem at first to be a crude, even rather childish procedure, and it certainly has limitations: but it has proved to be extraordinarily useful. Machines are the products of our brains and hands. We therefore understand them thoroughly and can speak conveniently about other things by comparing them with machines. The conception of living bodies as machines, having, as we say, 'structures' and 'functions', is at the basis of the whole modern development of biology and medicine.

Let us consider what happens in the nervous system in

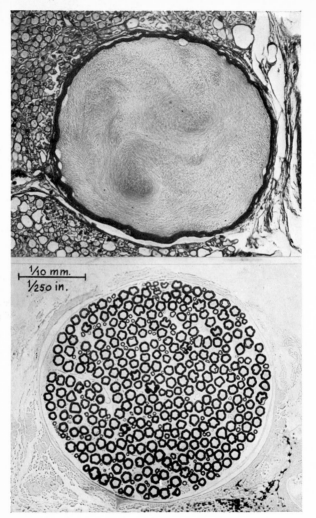

FIG. 1. *Above*. Single nerve fibre of the squid which controls the muscles that produce the jet propulsion. Smaller receptor nerve fibres are also seen. The large fibre conducts at about 50 miles per hour. Its sheath is thin in proportion to its size.

Below. Nerve controlling the calf muscle of a rabbit, shown at the same magnification as the squid's nerve. There are about 400 fibres in this nerve, each surrounded by an insulating sheath that gives a speed of conduction of 200 m.p.h. in these small fibres.

a typical case, such as blinking when a hand is waved in front of the eye. Such actions involve first a stimulus, the waving hand, which activates a receptor, the eye. From this receptor messages, known as nerve-impulses, pass along the nerves to the brain and from there other impulses are reflected back to the muscles of the eyelids. Such circuits are known as reflex arcs, and they ensure that the body shall do something appropriate when there is a change in its neighbourhood— the change being known as the stimulus. All the parts involved in the reflex arc are made up, like other parts of the body, of cells that can be seen with a microscope. Each cell is a separate little system, closed in, as the name implies, by a surrounding wall. This wall regulates everything that goes into or out of the cell. The nerve-cells are very long threads, drawn out to make nerve-fibres, which reach from, say, the toes to the spinal cord in the middle of the back. Each fibre is very thin, less than a thousandth of an inch across, although of course it is several feet long. The fibres run in bundles, tens of thousands of little thin threads, making up the nerves that connect the outer parts of the body, say arms or legs, with the brain (Fig. 1). Some of them are sensory or as we may say input threads; they carry impulses from the skin upwards to the brain. Others are motor or output fibres, carrying impulses down from the brain to the muscles. Each ingoing fibre is connected at its outer end with some part of the surface of the body; it will therefore be made to carry impulses only when a certain small area, say the tip of a finger, is touched (Fig. 7). The thousands of fibres together thus serve to bring to the brain a traffic of information about what is happening all over the surface of the body.

A great deal is known about the changes that happen in the nerve-fibres when they conduct. The whole process depends on the fact that there is a difference between the inside of a nerve-cell and the liquid around it. It is the function of the walls of the cell to maintain the difference. Often when different things are separated by boundaries there occur the phenomena that we call electrical charges. The drops of rain in a thunder-cloud are like this, and so are the plates in an accumulator. Everyone knows that such electrical charges may be discharged, with all sorts of effects from flashes of lightning to the starting of a motor-car. The nerve-fibre, because of the difference between its inside and outside, carries such an electric charge. What the stimulus does, say in the skin when a pin sticks into you, is to start a minute electrical discharge. This little discharge then makes the neighbouring part of the nerve-fibre discharge, and this in its turn the next part, and so on. That is how the nerve-impulse travels along the nerve-fibre, at a speed of about 200 miles per hour.

All this is very interesting, but it clearly does not tell us everything about how the nervous system works. It tells us how the nerves conduct, but not what happens when the impulses reach the central nervous system. We know that there are special outgoing or motor nerve cells that carry nerve-impulses to the muscles and make them act. But what decides which muscles shall act? If each ingoing nerve-fibre was connected with one outgoing fibre the body would work like your front-door bell. Once the button has been pressed only one thing can happen; if the system is in order, the bell must ring. But the body is not nearly so simple: it does not do the same thing every time it is stimulated. For example, if your son has got under the table without you knowing it and tickles your leg you will draw it away. Perhaps you will do that a second and even a third time. Then you will put your hand down to find out what is wrong. At about the fourth or fifth time you will catch him at it, and your response will be quite different from the first one. Your nervous system cannot be exactly like the bell system, which always works in the same way each time the button is pressed.

Sir Charles Sherrington has done more than anyone else to enlighten us in these matters. After prolonged study of the reflex responses of cats and other animals, he and his

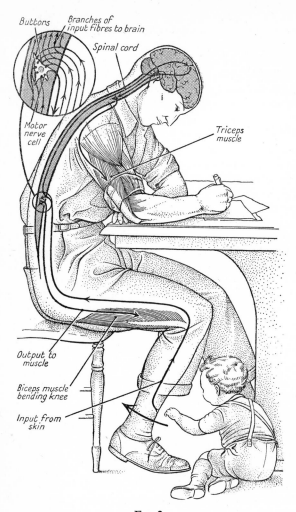

Buttons
Branches of input fibres to brain
Spinal cord
Motor nerve cell
Triceps muscle
Output to muscle
Biceps muscle bending knee
Input from skin

FIG. 2.

colleagues came to the following conception. Each muscle, say one of those that draws away the leg, is controlled by some hundreds of outgoing nerve-fibres (Fig. 2). It only exerts its full action if these are all set off together. Obviously the strength of its action will depend upon how many of the motor cells start to send out impulses along their fibres. Each motor nerve-cell gets connexions not from just one input source, like the front-door bell, but from several (Fig. 7). Whether a given motor cell sends out its impulses or not depends simply on whether it receives impulses from a sufficient number of sources. It is like a bell that only rings if a number of buttons are pressed at the same time. The first time your son tickles you a few impulses are sent in and they get through to the muscles that bend the knee; you draw away so that the stimulus ceases. The second time likewise. These first movements involve only a simple reflex action, all the connexions are made through the spinal cord alone. But impulses also go up to the brain each time, because there are side channels leading to it from the input fibres. Each time these inputs reach the brain they disturb it a little more, and at the third or fourth tickle the brain begins to send back impulses that reach to other muscles, probably to muscles of the arms as well as the legs, and produce a new set of actions.

Our next problem is now to try to see whether we can make out how the brain produces these more complicated actions. This is difficult in man and it may help, therefore, to describe first the case of an animal, for example the octopus, which Mr. Boycott and I have studied at Naples, where they are plentiful and can easily be kept in the tanks of the great zoological station there. An octopus in a tank always makes a home for itself in a corner, using any bricks or stones that may be lying about. If the octopus is outside its home and is stung by a sea-anemone, or given a small electric shock, it will retreat back into its home. It also retreats if a large object, say a dogfish, suddenly appears. On the other hand, if you put a crab into the tank, the

FIG. 3. Octopus making its first attack on crab and white plate, just before it receives an electric shock.

octopus will come out of its lair and hurl itself upon it, seizing it with its arms and returning home to eat it (Fig. 3). What comparisons can we use to describe the nervous mechanism by which the octopus steers away from a dangerous object but moves towards a source of food? Descartes, you remember, compared the body with a clock, the best self-regulating system that he knew. Today we have a large range of mechanical self-regulating devices, and therefore we can make much more interesting comparisons. The ball governors of steam-engines and the regulators of gas ovens and refrigerators are examples. Their value is that they keep the engine or the gas oven close to some particular state. This is obviously very much what living things do. Their life consists of a series of acts of regulation tending to keep the body in a certain state—to keep it alive. When there is some change, either within the body or near it, a reflex circuit goes into action to restore the *status quo*. Each of the reflexes is a kind of governor. It may make the body do something faster or slower, for instance by quickening the heart-beat when we run, or it may start an action that alters the outside world so as to abolish the source of change, as when we brush away a fly.

In recent years engineers have gone a lot farther in the design of self-regulating devices. They have produced a great variety of direction-finders and distance-finders, culminating in guided missiles and guided rockets. These devices do very much what the brain of the octopus does, they aim the missile at a target. Until not very long ago, aiming a gun involved human gunners. At first the aiming system consisted of relatively crude plans for sending back information about a target (say from a balloon), working out the appropriate ranging on paper or with a slide rule, and laying the gun by hand. But, gradually, calculating machines were devised that received the information, automatically computed the range and laid the gun on the target. From this it is only one stage to placing the whole apparatus for reception, calculation, and aiming within the missile itself, which is

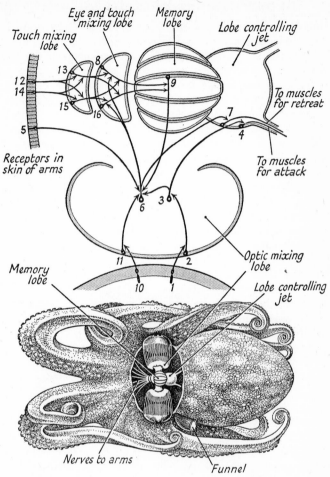

Touch mixing lobe

Eye and touch mixing lobe

Memory lobe

Lobe controlling jet

Touch mixing lobe

8

13

12
14

9

To muscles for retreat

15

16

7
4

5

To muscles for attack

Receptors in skin of arms

6   3

11   2

10   1

Optic mixing lobe

Memory lobe

Lobe controlling jet

Nerves to arms

Funnel

FIG. 4. DIAGRAM OF THE NERVOUS SYSTEM OF AN OCTOPUS

Below is a drawing of a dissection to show the position of the parts of the nervous system in the animal.

Above is a diagram of the pathways that are concerned in the learn-

[continued at foot of opposite page.

thus able to follow its target around and hit it. To be effective the machine may have to pick up information about a lot of things, not only the position of its target but also the direction and velocity of the wind and other such factors. Quite an elaborate calculating machine may then be needed in the missile, its brain as it were, to predict the correct course from all this information.

What is the value of comparing an octopus with a guided rocket of this sort? Clearly the two are not identical; there is only a very limited sense in which we can say that an octopus *is* a guided missile. People who have not thought carefully about the use of analogies are apt to take them too literally and to think that by comparing something with something else you can in a subtle way grasp, as they say, what it *really* is. This belief in the magic of comparison and of words has indeed a certain justification because, as will become increasingly clear in these lectures, man is so much a communicating animal that when he has put his experience into words we can say that it becomes more 'real' for him. The point is that comparing something unknown with something already known makes it possible to talk about the unknown. The value of making the analogy is that it facilitates communication.

We still cannot describe exactly how the nervous system

---

ing process. When a few retinal cells are stimulated the impulses pass through pathways such as 1, 2, 3, 4 and the jet sends the animal forwards.

An electric shock to the skin activates pathways such as 5, 6, 7, which puts the jet in the position for retreat. If a white square was showing at the same time this also starts up the cycle 6, 8, 9, 6, which keeps a group of cells such as 6 sensitive to the white square pattern, so that this now produces retreat if shown. This scheme does not show how the octopus discriminates the crab alone from the crab and square, but pathways 10, 11, 6, and 1, 2, 3, 6 show the sort of way in which optic impulses could combine to produce this result. In a similar way 12, 13 and 14, 15 allow for combinations in the touch mixing lobe.

It is essential to remember that the paths shown are only representatives of the tens of thousands of similar ones in each lobe.

works in the octopus, but we find it helpful in trying to do so to speak of the actions of its brain as an engineer would describe the parts of a guided missile. When a crab moves in front of the eyes of the octopus we say that the retina of the octopus' eye, acting as a receiver, sends information, in the form of nerve-impulses, along tens of thousands of nerve-fibres. These impulses then set up activities among further thousands of cells in parts of the brain that are called the optic lobes (Fig. 4). We know all too little about these activities, but comparison with the machinery of the guided missile is helping us to analyse them. The process is essentially one of using the information provided by the eyes for selection of a correct response, then predicting the course of the crab and steering towards it. The most difficult part for us to understand is the selection of the right response; what makes the octopus steer towards a crab but away from a shark? Some of the most recent calculating machines come close to making such decisions. I shall show in later lectures what hints we can get from the way that they do it. It is quite possible for us to imagine that when the optic lobes have completed their calculating the appropriate muscles are set into action. The octopus turns its head so as to fix one eye on the crab and then its arms and funnel are brought into play to propel it through the water and to steer it correctly until it hits its prey.

On the other hand, when a large object comes into the field of vision of the octopus the nervous system makes a different calculation and steers the animal back to its home. If the object, say a dogfish, comes nearer still, a further calculation is made and the octopus suddenly flattens, spreads itself out, and turns white except for the edges of its arms and the area around the eyes, which go very dark (Fig. 6). This pattern that it shows is a very striking one and would make an attacking animal retreat. Our guided missile analogy can help us to understand this too. The octopus system is such that when a large object appears in front of its eyes the action that is called for by the brain

FIG. 5. Octopus making a second attack on crab and white plate just after it has received a shock. The attack is slow and cautious and the animal is showing a pattern of light and dark marks.

computor is first retreat and then the production of the startling pattern. No doubt ideas of similar systems have occurred to the designers of weapons. In modern war one guided missile will be set to chase another; it should be possible for a rocket fired in London against an enemy rocket to act upon the attacker so as to turn it around and send it home again. This is just what the octopus does when it puts into action its device for, as we say in another idiom, frightening away the attacker.

So the guided missile analogy gives us some good terms with which we can usefully talk about the changes in the brain that ensure that the octopus will attack a crab or frighten away a big fish. Are there other aspects of its behaviour that are even harder to describe? There is the fact that the animal may change its behaviour in the light of past experience. In other words, the octopus can learn. Boycott and I were able to show this by putting in front of the animal a small white square together with a crab. The octopus attacked this combination quite readily, but things were so arranged that when it did so it received a small electric shock and withdrew quickly to its home. The next time that we put the crab and the square in front of it, the octopus came out much more slowly. Instead of hurling itself on the crab it put out its arms gingerly, as if to try to get the food without touching the white square (Fig. 6). When it finally attacked, it received another electric shock. After two or three such experiences the octopus remained at home when the white square was presented to it with the crab. But it continued to come out and eat crabs put in alone, without the white square.

If we are to compare the octopus with a machine, it must therefore be with one that can change its behaviour as the result of a memory that acts, as it were, as a store of past events. In recent years there has been a great development of calculating or computing machines that can store their results, in other words remember them and use them again later on. There is nothing essentially mysterious about such machines. Indeed, storing information is really quite a familiar process. The painter does it in his picture, the writer in his book, the photographer in his photograph. A card index, again, is a store of information. Imagine a machine that can put information into a card index and later take it out again. The cards with holes punched round the edges, which are used by some businesses, are devices for doing just this. One machine punches the cards according to a plan, in order to make them carry the information. Another machine can select all the cards punched in a certain place, corresponding, say, to all names beginning with the letter A. These are the cruder sorts of information stores, they are only partly automatic, like the hand-laid gun. Engineers can do much better now. Photographs and cards are bulky, they take a long time to make and to find and can only be used once. A good memory system for a machine employs units that can be used over and over again, are quickly marked, quickly found, and if necessary quickly erased. In modern calculating machines there are various systems, but they mostly depend not on making any permanent physical mark but on setting up some electrical action or process.

Information can be stored just as easily by starting up some continuous process as by photography or by punching a card. What is needed is some arrangement that sends messages that ultimately come back to their starting-point, and then sends them out again, and so on. For instance, you could store a piece of information, say your name and address, by turning it into a code of dots and dashes, like a telegram, and then arranging that it was sent on the wires from London to Bristol, Bristol to Birmingham, Birmingham to Edinburgh, Edinburgh to York, York back to London, and then on again to Bristol and so on round and round for days or years if necessary. All that is necessary for such storage is continual activity of the system, and a sufficient delay time, so that the sending machine has finished transmitting the message before it comes back to it. You might say, 'What an absurd method of storing—much better write it down and be done with it.' Actually, with suitably designed delay circuits (of course using other methods than sending telegrams all round the country) large amounts of information can readily be stored in this way. It has the great advantage that the information is readily available for reference or can be wiped out of the system, leaving no trace. No files of used photographs or cards remain. The apparatus is ready to store some more information.

'But', you may say, 'surely you don't expect us to compare the brain of an octopus or a man with a card index or a cycle of telegrams?' Only in a general way. It is the method of talking about things that matters, not the details. With the aid of such comparison we may be able to discover what change it is in the brain that constitutes the memory. We can look to see whether there is in the brain any sign of arrangements that could either print information or store it on continuous circuits. In the case of the octopus we have been able in our experiments to make one further step forward by finding a part of the brain that is necessary for the storing. There are two lobes on the very top of an octopus's brain that I have not yet mentioned (Fig. 4). A lot of nerve-fibres carry impulses to them from the optic lobes, and they send impulses back to the optic lobes. There is here therefore a circuit that could keep going in the way I have suggested. Boycott removed these uppermost lobes from some octopus under anaesthetic after they had learned not to attack when the white plate showed. After such an operation it was found that the animals no longer remembered the lesson. Each time that the crab and plate were shown the octopus came dashing out from the home and received a shock. So far as we have been able to discover, removing these lobes does not produce any other defect. The octopus eats well and appears perfectly normal, except that it has lost its power of memory. It seems therefore that these lobes are essential for storing information received. How do they do it? We do not know for certain, in the octopus or in any other animal, but it seems likely that the method of storing involves in some way the setting up of continuous processes such as those suggested in the telegraph analogy.

However it is very difficult to believe that in man all our memories depend only on keeping up some kind of race like this, year in year out, around our brains. If that was the method, anything that stopped the cycles would destroy all memory completely. Yet we keep our memories, not only in sleep, but under anaesthetics. After severe changes in the brain action, such as are produced by concussion, epileptic fits, or electric shock treatment, the memory is usually disturbed, but is not completely abolished, except perhaps for a short time. For such reasons, many physiologists have supposed that memory cannot depend on circles of activity and must be more like that provided by photography or punched cards in that some kind of image is left printed, as it were, on the brain tissue. Our recent research has indeed shown some basis for supposing that activity does leave its mark on the brain. There is evidence that the cells of our brains literally develop and grow bigger with use, and atrophy or waste away with disuse (see p. 83). It may be therefore that every action leaves some permanent print upon the nervous tissue.

Although we must admit that we do not know exactly how the memory is stored it seems possible that both the suggested processes are involved. It can hardly be an accident that the parts of the brain concerned contain, both in octopus and man, circular chains of action. It is conceivable that such circuits serve, as it were, to carry the memory for long enough to allow slight changes in the sizes or other features of the nerve-fibres to be produced, and so for the memory to be printed on the brain. To use our analogy of the tele-grams going round the country, we might imagine a tele-printer device, say in London, that made a punch card or photograph of the morse code message, but that needed several exposures to do it. Each time the message came round to London it would make the record a little more definite, so that finally the message would be retained even if the circula-

Fɪɢ. 6. The octopus has received several shocks from the white plate and instead of attacking now retreats into its home and shows a 'startling' pattern, in which the background becomes pale, but a dark edge appears round the arms and the eyes turn dark. The funnel is producing a jet of water directed so as to blow away the attacker.

tion stopped. Perhaps it is significant, in this connexion, that concussion or other shocks upset the memory of things that were going on just before the shock—the ones that were half printed, as it were, at the time. The worse the shock, the longer the time before concussion that is forgotten. Incidentally, the memory recovers also in a time sequence; if the forgetting reached back two weeks, then memory will gradually return from that point onwards to the moment of concussion. Even if we do not yet know all about the process of learning, there is at least evidence that memory has some basis in the activities going on in certain particular parts of the brain. It is a fascinating problem searching out the exact details of the changes that go on as we learn.

One further point should be emphasized: enormous numbers of separate units, the nerve-cells, are involved. All animals that show good learning powers have large numbers of short nerve-cells in their brain. We do not know what the system employed for storage may be, but it seems to depend on the presence of great numbers of small cells. The latest mechanical calculator in America has 23,000 valves. But the cortex of the human brain has nearly 15,000,000,000 cells. A computor with so many parts is beyond the dreams of the engineer. A huge building would be needed to house so many valves and all the water of Niagara would not be enough to work and cool them. Yet all that such a machine can do, and much more, goes on gently, gently in every human head, using very little energy and generating hardly any heat.

The purpose of this lecture has been to make you familiar with the approach of the biologist, who tries to study animals by finding out how they work. It has often been objected that this is only one way, a partial way and even, it is sometimes alleged, a poor way of studying them. Let me at once admit that it is certainly not the only possible way. Anyone who wishes is at liberty to start discussing the behaviour of the octopus with such phrases as 'It *wants* the food', 'It *feels* the shock', 'It *fears* the square', 'It *remembers* its pain', and so on. These may even seem to be more 'natural' ways of speaking about such matters. They make use of a method of speaking that is very ancient, depending on the assumption that in every octopus there sits some sort of person at least vaguely like a man. This way of talking therefore depends on comparison and analogy, just as much as does the machine talk. The scientist would say that such animistic systems are primitive, and he would claim that they are inefficient. They do not tell us anything about the inner workings of the creature or how to correct them if they are out of order. It may not matter much if with talk about the 'mind' of an octopus we are not able to cure its neuroses. But it does matter when we are talking about men.

Comment on the Second Lecture

THIS lecture more perhaps than any of the others suffers from the limitation of trying to provide too much information in a short time. In it I have tried to give the essentials of our knowledge about how the nervous system works. It would be hard enough to compress in this way all that we know about the units involved, the nerve-fibres and the impulses that they carry, but I had to force far more into this lecture. It also tries to provide a conception of how the nerve-fibres are arranged to provide the functioning units—the reflex arcs; then, in order to show how these operate in life, I hurried on to speak about the octopus and its habits. Up to that point the lecture had at least a reasonably familiar basis in showing how the physiologist describes the working of the body as he would a machine. But the final section tries to trace how the nervous system changes its characteristics by the process of learning. The machines with which we are most familiar have a fixed performance, they do not learn. I was therefore bound to introduce here some description of the newer types of machine that *do* learn, and to show how we may compare animals with them.

This great condensation may have made the lecture a difficult one to follow, but nevertheless I do not regret having concentrated so much into it. Indeed to do so was part of the plan of the whole series. I did not want listeners at any time to feel that they were hearing only details about this or that narrow scientific subject, but to try to make them see how scientific language can be used to study every aspect of man. The theme of this second lecture therefore is that we can usefully speak by comparison with machines even about such aspects of life as memory, which we are more accustomed to think of in other ways.

The comparison with the octopus was not introduced only because I am personally familiar with the nervous system of that animal. There was a more subtle reason. We do not find it easy suddenly to change our ways of speaking about ourselves—say about our memories. But to speak of the memory of an octopus is already so absurd—almost laughable—that it is hardly a more unnatural step to compare it with the memory of a machine. The whole point of our new scientific way of speaking is that it does not describe everything only in terms of man, as we are accustomed to do. Therefore it is easier to learn this habit by applying it to two unfamiliar things, such as octopuses and guided missiles, than it would be to try it straightaway on ourselves. In speaking thus of the memory of an octopus one does not have to unlearn first all the familiar ways of speaking, as we have to do before we can speak scientifically about the memory of man.

The details of the behaviour of the octopus may be intriguing, but they are not essential to the argument. I shall resist the temptation to expand on them here. But the compression in this lecture has inevitably made the account of the basic functioning of the nervous system a somewhat sketchy one and it may be worth while to amplify it here by saying more about nerve-impulses and reflex arcs. The greater part of our knowledge about how the nervous system works has come from study not of the brain itself but of the nerves that lead to and from it. These nerves are relatively firm structures that can be pulled about and experimented on easily. One can get some notion of this from the fact that nerves look so much like the tendons that the name 'nerve' is actually an adaptation of the Greek word for a sinew or tendon. Pieces of nerve can be removed completely from the body and yet retain their ability to conduct nerve-impulses. Physiologists have therefore preferred to study these convenient objects, rather than the very soft brain tissue, which is difficult to handle and changes its characteristics when its supply of blood is interfered with.

Further, the action of the nerves is fairly simple, whereas that of the brain is immensely complicated. It has been very profitable to begin the attempt to find new scientific language about a subject by looking at the simple things first and finding the units with which the system works. The unit of action of peripheral nerves is the nerve-impulse and physiologists hope that after having learned a lot about nerve-impulses in the nerves they will be able to go on to study how these impulses interact when they reach the brain. This is a good programme only up to a point; it requires two reservations. The first is that we must not wait too long before getting to work on the brain. A glance through any learned physiological journal shows that most of the work still deals only with the nerves. The second reservation is that we must not assume that we shall understand the brain only in the terms we have learned to use for the nerves. The function of nerves is to carry impulses—like telegraph wires. The function of brains is something else—later lectures try to show what. It would probably be wiser now to get to work on brains *even more than on nerves*, and many physiologists are doing this.

Certainly studies of the nerves have been of the very greatest value, because they have shown us a great deal about the way the nervous system works by transmitting information in a code of nerve-impulses. It would be relevant to the theme of the lectures to follow the progress of knowledge on this subject, which has developed hand in hand with improvement in methods for studying small electric currents. The battery that the surface of each nerve-fibre provides (p. 26) gives a difference of potential of about $\frac{1}{10}$th of a volt—compared to the 2–4 volts of small electric torch batteries. This is not a very small voltage, but it has not been as easy as might be expected to study it.

Nerves are not well-insulated, rigid things like dry cells. They are soft and watery and it has been no easy matter to find ways of attaching recording instruments to them, as we do to the terminals of a battery when we want to examine its voltage. The difficulty will be very apparent when you remember that the electric potential difference is between the inside and the outside of a nerve-fibre, a structure that in man and most animals is only 1/1,000th of an inch across. To measure the difference properly, therefore, we have to connect one of our terminals actually with the inside of this very narrow thread. There are various ways of doing this indirectly, but the only really satisfactory way is to push a wire along inside the nerve-fibre. This would be very difficult to do with human nerves, but we have been helped by the fact that a few animals have much larger nerve-fibres. The squids are relatives of the octopus and like these latter move along by squirting water from a sack—in fact by jet propulsion. The muscles that produce the jet are put into action by some enormous nerve-fibres, each nearly 1/10th of an inch thick (Fig. 1). These large fibres are, of course, much easier to work with than the very narrow fibres of mammals or frogs. Hodgkin and Huxley first showed that it is possible to push a wire inside such a fibre without killing it, and so to measure the voltage and the way it varies when the nerve conducts impulses. Moreover, one can actually squeeze out the inside part and analyse its contents, which are found to contain far more of the substance potassium than does the liquid outside the fibres and far less sodium. This is the difference that was referred to in the lecture as making the fibre into a battery. Hodgkin has now gone on to prove that as the nerve-impulses sweep along the nerve-fibre some potassium leaks out and some sodium leaks in at each point. If the nerve is made to conduct a great many impulses its battery gradually runs down, but in life of course it is continually recharged by an elaborate system that pumps the sodium out again and lets potassium in. This, like all pumping operations, involves doing work, the energy for which comes from the food that is eaten and combined with the oxygen taken in during breathing—a process analogous to the burning of coal in a fire. These details may give some idea of how far the physiologist can go in talking about the action of a part of the body by comparison with processes that occur outside the body, and especially in man-made machines.

However, for the purposes of the present discussion it is the way that the impulses carry information along the nerves that is important. The whole animal depends on these messages to ensure that its actions are appropriate to the events in the world around it. Obviously one requirement is that the speed of conduction should be adequate. Electric currents travel along wires at a tremendous speed, but the method of propagation used in nerves is for each stretch of the fibre to discharge and for the current so produced to fire off the next stretch, and so on. This provides conduction at a relatively slow rate and animals have adopted various devices for speeding it up. One of these is to increase the size of the conductors. The big nerve-fibres of the squid conduct at about 50 miles an hour, which is much faster than small fibres in the same animal. In this way messages can travel quickly to the animal's muscles and enable it to dart away from danger or towards its prey. Large nerve-fibres are found in many other animals that perform quick movements. When you tread on a worm and it retracts with a sudden jerk it uses a giant nerve-fibre for the purpose. Anyone who has tried digging for marine worms on a beach knows how quickly they withdraw.

The obvious disadvantage of large fibres is that they take up a lot of room. Big fibres are quite suitable for initiating mass actions, such as the jet of a squid or the withdrawal of a worm, where one nerve-fibre can carry impulses to a great many muscle-fibres and cause them all to shorten at once. Such actions are simple and they can be controlled by single fibres, carrying little information. But delicate movements, say writing, would be impossible if all the muscle-fibres contracted at once. For such movements it is necessary to have many thousands of nerve-fibres, each controlling only a small amount of muscle. If each of our nerve-fibres was $\frac{1}{10}$ inch across, like those of the squid, the whole bundle of them necessary even to control the fingers would be thicker than the arm. Fig. 1 shows that in a mammal or man the nerve-fibres are very much smaller, but each one of them is surrounded by a layer of fatty material that acts as an insulating sheath. This sheath has the effect of making the conduction faster, so that these small fibres conduct at up to 200 m.p.h. Since they are small we can have many thousands of them to carry impulses up from the receptor organs to the brain and down again to the muscles.

The fact that a great many nerve-fibres are needed gives us at once an important insight into the system of coding with which the nervous system works. In a telephone system a single wire can carry all the information necessary to reproduce the human voice. This is because there is a great range of fluctuation in the pulses of current that the wire carries. A single nerve-fibre could not possibly carry the human voice because it has only a very simple way of acting, it can only either respond, or not respond. One way of expressing this is to compare the nerve-fibre with a train of gunpowder: it can either fire or not at each point. If it carries along a message at all it carries its complete message. Nerve-impulses pass either wholly or not at all, and they cannot, therefore, become larger or smaller or vary in any way so as to follow the stimulus applied to them, as the pulses in a telephone wire can do. Physiologists call this the all-or-nothing law of conduction. When any receptor organ is stimulated, say by a pinprick in the skin, or a spot of light on the retina of the eye, the nerve-fibre connected with it carries a series of impulses, each exactly like the one before. These can be recorded by suitable means and appear as in Fig. 7, where each spike means that an impulse has passed a particular point on a nerve-fibre. Notice that they are all of approximately the same height, like a series of little equal explosions.

A single fibre conducting in this way can only carry a small amount of information, just as one can only signal very imperfectly if all the messages you can send are a series of identical taps on a drum. The nervous system works only with dots, not even with dots and dashes as does the morse code. But suppose you had ten thousand drums and that the rhythm of taps on each of them meant something different, then you could transmit quite a lot of information. This is how the nervous system works. All over the surface of the body are tens of thousands of receptors, each sensitive to one sort of change, such as touch or rise or fall of temperature. In the eyes, ears, and nose there are millions more. For example, the centre of the retina of each eye has nearly half a million sensitive cells, known as cones, each connected with a nerve-fibre. When the amount of light falling on any cone changes, the number of impulses passing along the nerve-fibre connected with it is either increased or decreased. All the cones and fibres together thus send to the brain detailed information about the pattern of light and shade that is focused on to the retina.

We have therefore a considerable knowledge of the way the whole system works. It uses very large numbers of receivers and of conductors. Each conductor operates in a rather simple way; it sends impulses of only one sort, varying the number sent per second, but nothing else. Throughout the nervous system we shall find the same plan, very many nerve-fibres or cells, each working in a simple way. In order to describe how a system like this works we have to use language that is rather different from that suitable for our ordinary machines, which have much fewer parts. Unless we are careful we shall forget that it is not the single units but their combined effect that is important for conveying the information. We have to find ways of speaking about the action of whole populations of cells, as well as about the individual ones. We are helped in this by the fact that science has already developed the mathematical language of statistics for other purposes, including that of describing human populations. In later lectures I suggest that we may be able to advance a long way by applying these statistical methods to the nerve-cells and their traffic of information.

The small amounts of information carried by each individual nerve-fibre only add together if at some point in the brain it is possible for the impulses in the different nerve-fibres to interact with each other. A great part of our problem

FIG. 7. Below, reconstruction of single motor nerve cell from the spinal cord of a cat. Small input fibres bring impulses to the cell and end as knobs attached to its receiving dendrites. When a sufficient number of input fibres work together the cell sends an output of impulses along its axon (A). The figure is based on a model made by R. Haggar and M. Barr and is reproduced with their permission.

The next five lines show a series of records of nerve impulses in a single nerve-fibre of the auditory nerve of a cat. Each time that an impulse passes along the fibre the electrical discharge causes an upward stroke to be recorded. The height of the stroke is proportional to the voltage of the discharge. The upper line shows that even with no noise the fibre is firing about 15 impulses per second. The other lines record the effect of louder and louder noises, which are produced by ringing a bell during the period marked by a white line below the impulses. The softest sound (second line) increases the frequency of the impulse discharged to about 25 per second and on the other lines it rises to 40, 70, and 100 impulses per second. The figures on the left show the loudness of the noise, measured in decibels; notice that the frequency of the impulses is approximately proportional to the loudness. The impulses are all of approximately the same size; there is a slight slow rhythmical change in their heights, which may be a characteristic of the recording apparatus rather than the ear. (Records reproduced by kind permission of Dr. H. Davis and the *Journal of Neurophysiology*.)

The lines at the top show the changes of electrical potential recorded by two wires attached to the touch receiving area of the cortex of a cat. The lines are traced by levers, which move up or down when the electrical conditions vary; the record reads from left to right. At the left both lines show the rather slow irregular rhythms of resting cortex. Then, as shown on the lowest line, light pressure was applied to the cat's toe. The potentials at the cortical points change as nerve impulses arrive from the fore-foot. The lower line shows the new type of activity until the foot pressure ceases, but the point recording on the upper line returns to its resting activity more quickly. (Reproduced with kind permission of Prof. E. D. Adrian.)

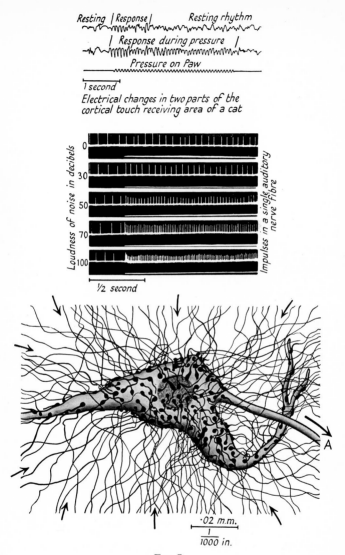

Resting | Response | Resting rhythm

| Response during pressure |

Pressure on Paw

1 second

Electrical changes in two parts of the
cortical touch receiving area of a cat

Loudness of noise in decibels

0

30

50

70

100

½ second

Impulses in a single auditory nerve fibre

A

·02 m.m.

1/1000 in.

FIG. 7.

is therefore obviously to trace out how the fibres run when they reach the central nervous system. A whole branch of anatomy is concerned with tracing connexions in the brain and the methods used for the purpose are most ingenious. Similarly, physiological studies have shown what motor effects follow from changing the input along particular bundles of nerve-fibres. Putting this anatomical and physiological evidence together we get a rather good picture of how some of the simpler parts of the nervous system work.

This picture really depends on finding out how the flow of incoming impulses controls the starting up of impulses in the outgoing or motor nerve-fibres. Fortunately we can actually see the region in which the connexions are made. Each nerve-cell has a number of receiving processes, its roots or dendrites (Fig. 7). All over the surface of each dendrite there can be seen rows of minute knobs. These are attached to the ends of fine nerve-fibres and are in fact the final terminals that bring the input impulses to the cell. No one knows exactly how many of the knobs end on the branches of each cell, but certainly there are many hundreds of them. We do not even know exactly where all the fibres ending in knobs come from (Fig. 2). Some bring impulses directly from receptors, say in the skin, but many impulses are also brought by fibres from the brain, which thus exerts direct control over the actions of the muscles.

The fact that impulses from various sources converge on to these cells provides the basis for the interaction that makes the information from the receptors useful. The essence of the situation is that impulses arriving from one or a few receptor sources are not sufficient to start off a train of impulses in the output fibre. The substance of the knob on the incoming fibre is not continuous with that of the dendrite and therefore nerve-impulses do not pass freely over from one to the other. The interposition of this gap, technically called a synapse, gives the nervous system some of its most important properties. Because of the presence of the synapse it is necessary in order to fire off impulses in the cells that there should

be an input from a considerable number of fibres, firing
approximately at the same time. In fact the firing of the
output cells depends on suitable spacing and timing of the
information carried by the input fibres. The cells and their
synapses provide as it were the detector or recipient that
puts together the information arriving along the many incoming fibres and produces a significant act.

Sherrington was able to show that not all of the input has
the effect of exciting the cells to carry impulses; some input
fibres have the opposite effect of quietening the cells down,
of inhibiting them. Each cell, therefore, is influenced by a
balance of excitatory and inhibitory states; whether it sends
impulses to its muscles depends on which influence pre-
dominates.

In order to complete our picture we have to think of all
the tens of thousands of nerve-cells in the spinal cord and
the input converging upon them from millions of receptor
fibres and fibres coming from the brain. It is not easy to
imagine so many channels; it is no wonder that we cannot
describe even what the spinal cord does as exactly as we can
describe how a clock works. Some of the connexions are
such that the input produces a rather fixed and definite
response, which we speak of as a reflex action. A hand
waved in front of the eye nearly always produces a blink;
a foot that treads on a tin-tack is quickly withdrawn. Even
these protective reflexes can be inhibited by the brain, however, and most other actions are controlled in a very elaborate
way by input from various sources. The remaining lectures
are concerned with trying to show how we can study all
the influences that come into play between input and output
in a complicated organism such as a man.

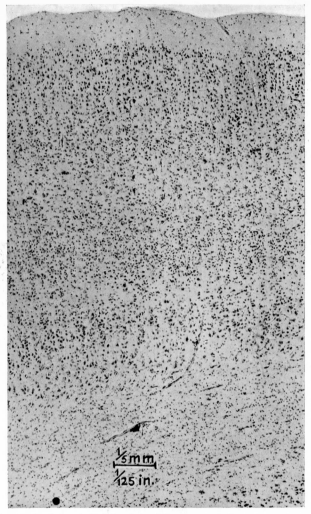

¹⁄₅ mm
¹⁄₁₂₅ in.

FIG. 8. Section of the visual receiving area of the cortex of man, stained to show the nuclei of all the cells present. The nerve fibres are not shown by this method.

Third Lecture

THE HUMAN CALCULATING MACHINE

IN order to have some picture of how the brain works it is useful to think of it as a gigantic government office—an enormous ministry, whose one aim and object is to preserve intact the country for which it is responsible. Ten million telegraph wires bring information to the office, coded in dots. These correspond to the sensory or input fibres reaching the brain. In the office one must try to imagine nearly 15,000,000,000 clerks, that is to say more than six times more people that there are at present in the whole world. They correspond to the cells of the brain, and we can imagine them sitting in closely packed rows, as the brain cells are arranged (Fig. 8). Every clerk has a telephone and receives coded messages either from outside the office or from some other part of it. So each nerve-cell of the brain receives nerve-impulses, either from the sense organs or from other brain cells near to it or far away. Each clerk spends most of his time sending code messages on his telephone to some other group, which may be near or far. So every nerve-cell has an out-going fibre, which may be long or short. But the clerks can also influence their neighbours by whispering 'silence'; obviously if a group of them starts doing this then a wave of quiet will pass over that area and it will send out no messages for a while.

In this way most elaborate patterns of activity will grow up between the huge numbers of clerks throughout the building. There are circuits by which messages are sent from one department to another and then back to the first and so on indefinitely. Messages will go round and round, but be influenced by incoming messages and by the waves of silence. However, the whole office is so arranged that some of the

telephones eventually transmit instructions to workers outside, directing them how to run the country and bring food,
drink, and other necessities to the government office. So
some of the brain cells carry impulses that control the actions
of the muscles, especially those of the hands, tongue,
and lips.

How would this office be organized, how would it convert
the information it received into orders for the governing of
the territory it controls? Everything, surely, would depend
on its having arrangements by which all relevant information
could be brought together to produce the right answer to
every question put to it. This is just what happens in the
nervous system. The sense organs transmit information to
whichever departments of the brain can use it. But how does
the brain bring this information together, so as to send out
the right orders to the territory it is responsible for—the
body? To find this out we may return to the comparison of
brains with calculating machines. Information reaches the
brain in a kind of code, you remember, of impulses passing
up the nerve-fibres. Information already received is stored in
the brain either by sending impulses round closed circuits, or
in some form corresponding to a print. This is just what
calculating machines do—they both store old information
and receive new information and questions in coded form.
The information received in the past forms the machine's
rules of action, coded and stored away for reference. When
asked a question, it puts it into code, and, by a process
that is essentially one of adding and subtracting very fast,
the machine can then refer the question to the rules that
are already stored in it, and so produce the right answer.
Similarly, the brain is constantly relating the new impulses
that reach it to the information already stored away in its
tissues. To show the closeness of the parallel, think of
a machine that would act as a cricket umpire. The wicket-
keeper has whipped off the bails and called 'How's that?'
A camera, rather like a television camera, turns the sequence
of events into a code of dots and dashes. The machine

already contains the rules of cricket, also in a code of dots and dashes. The machine could now proceed to fit together the coded report of the situation and the rules and answer with the word 'Out'. No such machine has in fact yet been built—but it might be. Its action would depend on being able to fit together the input from the camera with the rules. Modern calculating machines can do this sort of thing because the code is all in a simple form like dots and dashes, actually 0's and 1's, and therefore involves adding and subtraction, though an enormous number of calculations may be necessary to determine the answer.

The brain has an even greater number of cells than there are valves in a calculator and it is not at all impossible that it acts quite like an adding machine, in some ways. In the second lecture I showed how the information was put into a code of nerve-impulses, and how there are circuits of activity that might constitute the memory. However, we still do not know exactly how the brain stores its rules or how it compares the input with them. It may use principles different from those of these machines.

It is convenient to consider that in the brain the calcula-tions are done at a series of different levels. The part of the brain just above the spinal cord, known as the medulla (Fig. 9), contains centres for regulating internal functions, such as breathing. These centres are vitally important for the working of the body. Even the smallest damage to them causes death within a few minutes. The surgeon, who is sometimes prepared to remove some of the so-called highest parts of the brain, avoids even the sight of these lower centres, and the thought of touching them fills him with alarm. It is correct, however, to call them lower—not because they are without importance, but because they are regulators of a rather simple type. The responses that they produce are reached by the combination of information coming from few sources. There are many such simpler centres in the brain, regulating such activities as breathing, the action of the heart, of the kidneys, of the amount of sugar in the blood, and so on. For these simple calculations relatively small numbers of nerve-cells are enough.

The next level of the brain that we may consider performs rather more complicated calculations. It is known as the hypothalamus and lies near the centre of the head. What goes on there has a profound influence on the well-being of each one of us. Injuries in this region produce changes of some aspect or other of the basic internal functions of the man or animal concerned. Thus one part of the hypothalamus controls temperature: injuries there may produce fevers. Another part controls appetite, and hence the amount of food consumed and whether we get fat. Still more elaborate functions controlled from here are the degree of activity or of sleepiness. One of the earliest clues to the action of the hypothalamus was that these centres are especially frequently damaged by the infectious disease known as sleepy sickness. The person's whole state of activity is altered and periods of days and perhaps weeks are passed in sleep. Even the most complicated of our activities are affected by the hypothalamus. It has been noticed that patients who have recovered from sleepy sickness often develop a marked change in their moral character—usually for the worse. Thus Professor Kennedy, among others, has recorded that a high proportion of children get into trouble with the police after sleepy sickness. Some of them seem to lack all moral sense. They may be restless, bored, or liable to sudden outbreaks of cruelty and aggressiveness, and are without a proper feeling of responsibility for others.

We must not jump to extreme conclusions and say that every delinquent is just a person with a diseased hypothalamus. Things are not nearly so simple as that. Other parts of the brain have a great deal to do with social behaviour. Indeed, the hypothalamus does not by any means work as a separate isolated unit. Professor Le Gros Clark and his colleagues have shown that there are numerous nerve-fibres conducting impulses in both directions between it and the uppermost parts of the brain. This corresponds to

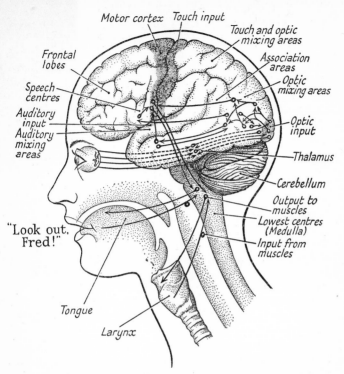

Motor cortex   Touch input

Touch and optic
mixing areas

Frontal
lobes

Association
areas

Optic
mixing areas

Speech
centres

Auditory
input

Optic
input

Auditory
mixing
areas

Thalamus

Cerebellum

Output to
muscles

"Look out,
Fred!"

Lowest centres
(Medulla)

Input from
muscles

Tongue

Larynx

FIG. 9. Diagram to show some of the pathways involved in a response such as shouting a warning to a child seen about to cross a road.

The inverted image thrown on to the retina of the eye causes a discharge of impulses in the optic nerves, which end in the thalamus. From here further impulses are sent to the cortex at the back of the head. The cells of this optic receiving area send impulses to the optic mixing areas and from here they go to many other parts of the cortex. The complicated activity thus set up fits with the existing brain rules to produce impulses in the output fibres of the cortex, such as those shown leading to the motor cells that activate the muscles of the tongue and larynx. The arrangements for providing feed-back at various stages are shown, including the receptors in the muscles.

Many other parts of the cortex would be involved besides those here drawn, and of course instead of the few cells shown millions would be active.

a fact which all of us know, that such conditions as aggressiveness or irritability, though partly independent of our intellectual life, yet both influence and can be controlled by it. The hypothalamus, therefore, is a place that receives nerve-impulses from the internal parts of the body. From this information its calculations establish the general attitude or direction of much of brain action—the emotional tone, as we might say.

But it does not control the details of what we do. That is the function of the great sheet of nerve-cells occupying the top of the head, the cerebral cortex. With its associated parts this makes our main calculating machine, containing thousands of millions of nerve-cells. This is the chief section of our great government office, and employs 99 per cent. of the clerks. This is the part of the brain that sifts the more complicated sorts of information sent in from the outside world and calculates what we shall say and what we shall do. Receiving the nervous messages sent in from the eyes, ears, and touch, it calculates suitable action by the hands and by the larynx and tongue in producing speech. In fact, if we could discover the patterns in which the cerebral cortex acts we should be well on the way to our aim of recognizing, as biologists should, the special means that man uses to obtain his living. Recalling our model of the government office, we shall be warned that the task will not be simple. Imagine trying to understand how an organization including several times more people than there are in the whole world is planned! Somehow or other the activities of all these millions of cells ensures that suitable actions are performed. Consider the case of the eyes. Nerve-fibres carry impulses from the retina to the centre of the brain. From there other fibres reach to a particular part of the cortex at the back of the head. Input produced even by a tiny spot of light on the retina—say from a star—will first influence a tiny area of cortex, but from that small area impulses will be sent far and wide through the cortex and eventually, if appropriate, will influence the fibres that make the voice muscles say 'star' (Fig. 9).

The major problem is to understand the pattern of the activities in the brain by which the input is fitted with the memory and produces the action. Consider, for instance, what happens when you call a friend by name across the street. The image of your friend on the retina of your eye sets up a disturbance in the brain, which results in speech. Our problem is to describe that brain disturbance. It is not a disturbance of a previously passive system, but of one already fully active. There is an elaborate pattern of activities going on in the brain. When a sense organ sends input that fits in some way into this brain pattern we respond by a suitable action.

The cortex, therefore, is our great calculating machine for fitting together the parts of the sensory input at any one time and comparing them with previous inputs. Experience has left its mark on the brain, giving it the rules with which it operates, giving it in fact a system of law, of certainty. We can imagine how the circles of messages between the clerks in our government office would control the manner of proceeding, depending, of course, on past experience. The pattern of this activity, together with the filing system of the office, would provide its memory. If the laws embedded in the brain machine are efficient they will enable every input produced by a disturbance outside to be fitted into some pattern that will produce an effective action. That is to say, they will make the muscles do something that will restore the body back to its steady state, the state, you remember, that all organisms tend to preserve.

This perhaps gives an inkling of the layout of the whole cortical system. I must emphasize again that I am giving only the very roughest outline; the details are of hardly imaginable complexity, and we have only begun to unravel them. We do not know much yet about what goes on in our brains and therefore cannot expect educators to educate them properly, psychologists to help us to correct their workings, or surgeons to know whether it is wise to cut pieces out of them. How can we find out more? We have a lot of apparently unconnected facts about the brain. We are seeking for a clue that will show how the facts are connected and will give us a good general scheme for understanding the plan of brain action. I believe that we shall find that clue by consideration of the nature of these patterns within the cortex. That is why I have spent so long giving analogies that may at least vaguely suggest what sort of patterns to look for. Meanwhile, what are the different sorts of evidence that we have to use as our clues? Being an anatomist, I have put what are commonly called the structural facts first, speaking of the arrangement of the cells.

We have, however, all sorts of further information about the brain—for instance, of its electrical activities. In 1929 it was discovered that if you make proper electrical connexions with the surface of the head, then you can show, with a suitable apparatus, that small changes of electrical potential are going on throughout the life of every person (Fig. 7). The activity of nervous conduction is accompanied by electrical changes, and there is no doubt that the electrical brain waves are in some way a sign of the activities of the brain cells. Probably, as Professor Adrian and others suggest, they are the result of many cells acting together. It may be significant that the waves are most clear when the brain is idling—for instance, when a person is asleep or daydreaming. Then, apparently, large masses of cells are working in unison. When the person wakes or begins to think, the electrical changes become more complicated. If only we could understand the patterns of these waves we should be much nearer to understanding what goes on in our heads. At present we can tell from the brain waves whether a person is awake or asleep, and detect some useful things about the brain—for instance in relation to epilepsy. But we cannot be said yet to be able to read a person's thoughts from his electrical brain waves.

Another whole set of information comes from experiments in which the brain is made to work by electrical stimulation. This is a great help in some cases during brain operations.

A pair of fine wires is placed on the brain surface, and small electrical charges are applied, which have the effect of starting the activity of the brain cells. In some brain operations it is best not to put the patient to sleep, but to use injections of local anaesthetics to prevent pain during the cutting of the skin and bone. The brain can thus be exposed while it is still in its normal waking state, and the person is sensible enough to stay still and can describe what he feels. It has been known for a long time that electrical activation of some parts of the cortex produces movements of various muscles. Sir Charles Sherrington had shown this by experiments on apes. Professor Penfield of Montreal confirmed that, in man, electrical stimulation of points on a strip of tissue down the side of the brain produces movements of the body. When the part of his body moves, the patient feels as if he *has* to move it; he does not say that he wills to do so. For instance, when the wires are on the part responsible for speech he may cry out rather like a baby. He is not in pain—stimulation of the cortex is never painful—he just feels, to his surprise, that he *must* cry out. If asked to try to stop he is unable to do so, and he is most intrigued by the whole business.

The area of cortex controlling each part of the body is by no means proportional to the size of that part. Thus, the area of the cortex that produces hand and finger movements is much bigger than the whole of that controlling the legs. The area for the lips and tongue is very large. There are also large areas whose stimulation stops the patient speaking. He later describes his experience by saying, 'My tongue suddenly felt paralysed', or, 'I just lost control of my lips'. In other cases he will say, 'I could not think any more'. Evidently the rather crude stimulus is not able to produce the complicated movements of speech; indeed it actually seems to disrupt the fine patterns of action of the nerve-cells that are responsible for speech. The extent of the cortex connected with each motor function is therefore proportional to the intricacy of the actions it performs. This fact, that such large areas are concerned with the muscles of speech, is direct confirmation of the thesis that man is primarily a communicating animal.

From stimulation of various areas there are reports of sensations—for example, flashes, balls of white or coloured lights or other vague dancing lights, seldom of well-formed or recognizable objects or pictures. Stimulation of the area responsible for hearing produces reports of sounds—buzzings, ringings, and knockings. These observations, therefore, confirm that the cortex deals predominantly with the receiving systems for touch, vision, and hearing. But the areas that respond in this way occupy less than half of the whole cortex. The remaining parts are of two sorts. First the silent areas, the frontal lobes of the brain, whose stimulation produces no response at all. Secondly there are certain parts known as association areas, whose stimulation sometimes produces complicated sensations and memories.

Further insight into the functions of the brain can be obtained from seeing what are the effects of the removal of the various parts, as a result of injury or surgery. I can only outline a few points of this fascinating story. Removal of part of the motor area produces severe paralysis of movement on the opposite side. Thus if a certain part of the left area is removed, the patient's right arm and hand will be completely paralysed at first. However, he will gradually recover, first the cruder movements of the whole arm, and then, gradually, some finer movements, though never his full original range of skill and dexterity. Severe damage, by an accident, of the receiving station in the cortex for messages from the eyes results in total and incurable blindness. Damage to the association areas mentioned above produces variable and complicated results. Sometimes the person is hardly changed by their loss, but in other cases there may be most curious defects. The patients may be able to recognize objects but not to name them, to name them but not to read their names, to read but not to write or vice versa, and so on. Injury in certain areas produces complete loss of speech. Evidently damage to these association areas upsets the pattern of action by which the brain produces communication. Evidently, also, this pattern varies, as we should expect, in different people. The rules by which the brain works are not inborn, they have in the main been learnt.

Some of the most interesting operations in which portions of the brain are removed have been those in which parts of the frontal lobes are severed from the rest. These lobes lie in front of the motor part of the cortex, and are the region of the brain that is very much bigger in man than in any animals. That is why we have a higher forehead than the apes. Yet separation of this front part produces neither loss of sensation nor motor paralysis. There are, however, slight changes of personality, changes that are usually in the direction of making the person more docile, often more communicative. The exact effects vary a good deal, however. Usually, after the operation there is no loss of any actual function or power, but there is not quite the level of performance and efficiency that is necessary for perfect conduct of the business of life in our society. We cannot say that we by any means fully understand the functioning of this most characteristically human part of the brain, but it seems that in some way it operates the balance between action and restraint that is necessary for social life. Its actions are therefore connected with what may be called the highest levels of communication. Their loss does not involve any alteration of the power to speak or to understand words. Without the frontal lobes a person can still enunciate words properly, but he uses them in socially wrong ways. After such operations patients sometimes became embarrassingly frank, even rude in behaviour.

We have therefore a mass of information about the functioning at various levels of the brain system that controls our behaviour. The information is quite new, and could hardly even have been imagined a hundred years ago. Yet it is still very scrappy, and it is important not to get the idea that we understand all about the brain. The information from different sources is only beginning to fit together. We cannot yet say that we have a clear model by means of which we can speak of how the cortex works. The electrical changes going on in it suggest that when it is at rest large numbers of cells beat together in unison. The effect of stimulation is to disturb this unison. Professor Lashley of Harvard, one of the ablest students of the brain, has suggested that we may compare the complicated waves of action thus started with the pattern of disturbances set up when stones fall on a sheet of water. This analogy, like that of the government office, which I used earlier, has the advantage of reminding us that we must concentrate attention on the *patterns* of action set up among the millions of cells of the brain. But we are only just beginning to be able to imagine what they may be like. We are still searching for analogies to help us to understand this 'enchanted loom', as Sir Charles Sherrington has called it.

From the very number of the analogies I have mentioned, you can see how doubtful we are in this present phase of scientific research. I have compared the brain with a government office, a calculating machine, and with the waves on the surface of water, and one could go on with many more analogies. This whole business of making comparisons may seem to you absurd and useless. It is, however, one of our chief aids to exploring the world and hence to getting a living. Indeed, I hope in later lectures to show that it is a tool we have been using in essentially the same way for thousands of years. For many purposes we have no other means of communication. It is not a question of whether or not to make comparisons but of which comparisons to make. We must use the rules—the certainties we have established by past experience. It is by comparison with these that each of us shapes his future. We *must* compare things, because that is the way our brains are constituted.

Fourth Lecture

THE ESTABLISHMENT OF CERTAINTY

IN one of his poems A. E. Housman expresses a feeling
we sometimes have; a feeling of being lost in the
Universe, of not *belonging* there:

> I, a stranger, and afraid,
> In a world I never made.

A world I never made? But the researches outlined in the
last two lectures show that the brain of each one of us does
literally create his or her own world. To explain this we must
answer the question: How does each brain set up its own
characteristic rules? How do those regular patterns of
activity in the cells of the brain described in the last lecture
develop? This is the process that I call the establishment
of certainty, and it is a process that we may consider as
beginning in each human being at the moment when, as
a newly born baby, his eyes open on to the world. He will
have received some stimuli before this, but now his brain
begins to receive a flood of information from all the senses.
From that moment the incoming stimuli begin to leave their
mark on the brain, its rules begin to be established. We have
no means of examining and recording all that happens in
the brains of babies and very young children. But we can
learn a great deal that is helpful from the reports of people
with certain rather rare forms of blindness who, though born
blind, have later been operated on and received their sight.
This is a specially favourable opportunity by which we may
examine, as it were, the phases of childhood being passed
through in a person who can talk.

What would such a person see; what would he say, on
first opening his eyes on a new world? During the present
century the operation has been done often enough for

systematic and accurate reports to be collected. The patient on opening his eyes for the first time gets little or no enjoyment; indeed, he finds the experience painful. He reports only a spinning mass of lights and colours. He proves to be quite unable to pick out objects by sight, to recognize what they are, or to name them. He has no conception of a space with objects in it, although he knows all about objects and their names by touch. 'Of course', you will say, 'he must take a little time to learn to recognize them by sight.' Not a *little* time, but a very, very long time, in fact, years. His brain has not been trained in the rules of seeing. We are not conscious that there are any such rules; we think that we see, as we say, 'naturally'. But we have in fact learned a whole set of rules during childhood.

If our blind man is to make use of his eyes he, too, must train his brain. How can this be done? Unless he is quite clever and very persistent he may never learn to make use of his eyes at all. At first he only experiences a mass of colour, but gradually he learns to distinguish shapes. When shown a patch of one colour placed on another he will quickly see that there is a difference between the patch and its surroundings. What he will not do is to recognize that he has seen that particular shape before, nor will he be able to give it its proper name. For example, one man when shown an orange a week after beginning to see said that it was gold. When asked, 'What shape is it?' he said, 'Let me touch it and I will tell you!' After doing so, he said that it was an orange. Then he looked long at it and said, 'Yes, I can see that it is round.' Shown next a blue square, he said it was blue and round. A triangle he also described as round. When the angles were pointed out to him he said, 'Ah. Yes, I understand now, one can *see* how they feel.' For many weeks and months after beginning to see, the person can only with great difficulty distinguish between the simplest shapes, such as a triangle and a square. If you ask him how he does it, he may say, 'Of course if I look carefully I see that there are three sharp turns at the edge of the one patch of light, and four on the other.' But he may add peevishly, 'What on earth do you mean by saying that it would be useful to know this? The difference is only very slight and it takes me a long time to work it out. I can do it much better with my fingers.' And if you show him the two next day he will be quite unable to say which is a triangle and which a square.

The patient often finds that the new sense brings only a feeling of uncertainty and he may refuse to make any attempt to use it unless forced to do so. He does not spontaneously attend to the details of shapes. He has not learned the rules, does not know which features are significant and useful for naming objects and conducting life. Remember that for him previously shapes have been named only after feeling the disposition of their edges by touch. However, if you can convince him that it is worth while, then, after weeks of practice, he will name simple objects by sight. At first they must be seen always in the same colour and at the same angle. One man having learned to name an egg, a potato, and a cube of sugar when he saw them, could not do it when they were put in yellow light. The lump of sugar was named when on the table but not when hung up in the air with a thread. However, such people can gradually learn; if sufficiently encouraged they may after some years develop a full visual life and be able even to read.

It takes at least a month to learn the names of even a few objects. Gradually the patient leaves out the laborious counting of the corners and comes to identify things so quickly that, as in an ordinary person, the process by which he does so is not apparent. So it is not that all along the eyes or brain were incapable of acting normally. What these people lack is the store of rules in the brain, rules usually learnt by the long years of exploration with the eyes during childhood. They have no models with which to compare the input, no mould or filter that can be used to select the significant features of visual experience and produce appropriate words and other motor responses. A normal person learns the rules of seeing by connecting some parts of the sensory input with motor acts that lead to satisfaction, for instance, naming and the fulfilment of communication.

We do not know exactly what happens in the brain as it learns to react to shapes during that period of training. At first the eyes wander at random over the visual field. Probably learning to move the eyes in certain ways is an important part of the process. Compare this with a very young animal wandering at large in the woods, with no clue as to where to find food. Each time he moves in a direction that results in satisfaction of his hunger a link is formed in his brain. This link makes him tend to repeat the movement on a later occasion. Similarly, when the once blind man is told that what he has so far seen as only a patch of light is in fact an orange, he learns that the movements of running his eyes round its outline are useful. His brain subsequently makes his eyes follow outlines, he becomes able to name objects by sight, with all the advantages of that communication.

So we can believe that the brain gradually comes to act in certain special ways. One of the earliest of these habits gives us the tendency for the eye to sweep along lines instead of in all directions at random. Connexions between the cells in the brain are built up, such that each time the eye rests on a point it tends to follow any lines away from that point. Thus we come to pick out and name the significant objects in the field of vision, neglecting vague shadows.

Certain difficulties familiar to everybody give hints of the way the brain is organized. There is no difficulty in learning that the words 'right' and 'left' refer to horizontal and 'up' and 'down' to vertical directions. But every child has some difficulty in distinguishing 'up' from 'down'. On the other hand, 'in' and 'out' are easily learned. Even as adults many of us have trouble with 'left' and 'right', and incidentally also east and west. These difficulties all suggest that the brain is organized in such a way that although our eyes readily sweep *either* from side to side *or* up and down, yet these two sets of movements are quite distinct. We never confuse 'up' or 'down' with 'right' or 'left', but there is no such deep distinction between sweeping from left to right and from right to left, and therefore we have difficulty in correctly naming these directions. We do not know what arrangement of the brain cells makes us select lines in this way, but we are beginning to suspect that there is such an arrangement (see p. 84).

From following lines an early step is to learn to attend to circles. There is certainly something about a circle that very readily attracts our eyes. We pick it out from a mass of other input reaching us. On advertisement hoardings the pictures often contain one or several circles—those who produce advertisements have excellent reasons for finding out what patterns attract the human eye. Designs of circles have played a prominent part in many art forms, as shown in any rose window in a church, for example. Evidently there is something about lines and circles that fits easily into the rules of our brain. When we see a line that makes three parts of a circle, or even less, we at once complete it and call it a circle. The brain cells are so arranged that their rules make a model or mould, which selects certain parts of the input for attention and naming.

The man born blind, when first given sight had only a lot of colours to look at, but no rules, no models to help him to abstract, to select significant features. Like all those who have not learned the point of abstracting, he could not believe that it was worth while trying to work out anything significant about these coloured patches. They did not seem to mean anything to him. So the paintings of Picasso mean nothing to his angry critics. The once blind man was like all of us in this. He already had his own rules, his own ways of selecting and communicating, using his sense of touch. He was content with these ways and could not see the point of trying to find others. 'And why not?' you may say. 'Why must anyone seek for new ways of acting?' The answer is that in the long run the continuity of life itself depends on the making of new experiments. As we go on with these lectures I hope that it will become plain how the continuous invention of new ways of observing is man's special secret of living. There is a limit to the extent to which this invention can go on in any one head, but the continuity of life of the whole race will only be preserved if the individual contributes his new invention to the rules that he passes on to others.

These most interesting observations on the difficulties of people born blind show that we have to learn from others how to see. The visual receiving system in its untrained state has only very limited powers. We are perhaps deceived by the fact that the eye is a sort of camera. Contrary to what we might suppose, the eyes and brain do not simply record in a sort of photographic manner the pictures that pass in front of us. The brain is not by any means a simple recording system like a film. Recognition of this fact of our relativity is one of the most revolutionary developments of the thought of the present time. Its importance is only now dawning upon us very gradually, and it is a main purpose of these lectures to show what the change means. Many of our affairs are conducted on the assumption that our sense organs provide us with an accurate record, independent of ourselves. What we are now beginning to realize is that much of this is an illusion; that we have to learn to see the world as we do.

These ways of acting that we learn give us a rhythm of behaviour. The brain of course is not a passive mass of tissue, through all waking life it drives along. Woken in the morning by some stimulus, it immediately begins to run through sequences of activities, according to the rules that it has learned. These sequences produce the actions by which the body lives. They are partly touched off by outside stimuli, but, once started, they may run by themselves as independent trains in the brain, each combination starting another one.

The life of the new-born child consists largely of sleep, of periods, that is, in which numerous brain cells are firing in unison. We know this because electrical records show that in a baby there are very large and regular brain waves. This unison or synchrony becomes broken up by the nerve-impulses arising from the receptor organs, internal or external. The receptors are so arranged as to alert the organism that its needs are not satisfied; it must be up and doing. The hungry baby wakes and cries, giving the sign stimulus that brings the mother's attention. At first it kicks and clutches at random, until it obtains the milk. When the stomach is filled, the hunger impulses from it stop, the brain returns to its simple synchronous activity, and the baby goes to sleep. But in the course of each waking episode there are changes going on in the brain. Actions, at first random, develop into little sequences, according to patterns developed during previous wakings, and these become printed or other-wise recorded in the brain.

Meanwhile the world does not stand still. The mother becomes gradually less co-operative and the child has to learn to get what it needs by ways other than crying. The eye movements are used to discriminate between faces, cups, and other objects, so that the output of the brain leads to the making of appropriate noises, the giving of names that produce satisfactory actions by others—that establish com-munication. The effect of stimulations, external or internal, is to break up the unison of action of some part or the whole of the brain. A speculative suggestion is that the disturbance in some way breaks the unity of the actual pattern that has been previously built up in the brain. The brain then selects those features from the input that tend to repair the model and to return the cells to their regular synchronous beating. I cannot pretend to be able to develop this idea of models in our brain in detail, but it has great possibilities in showing how we tend to fit ourselves to the world and the world to ourselves (see p. 86). In some way the brain initiates sequences of actions that tend to return it to its rhythmic pattern, this return being the act of consummation, or completion. If the first action performed fails to do this, fails that is to stop the original disturbance, then other sequences may be tried. The brain runs through its rules one after another, matching the input with its various models until somehow unison is achieved. This may perhaps only be after strenuous, varied, and prolonged searching. During this random activity further connexions and action patterns are formed and they in turn will determine future sequences.

As the child grows, therefore, the brain acquires a series of ways of acting, of laws as it were, for dealing with the situations that occur to it. The sequence of natural events around us is rhythmic. Night succeeds day, and night is a poor time for an animal that mainly depends on its eyes. Therefore we normally sleep by night and wake by day. But notice that this rhythm has to be learned by the child and can be modified and if necessary reversed in the adult.

The actual process of association between two inputs to the brain is probably performed rather rapidly in all animals. It was mentioned earlier that an octopus learns after only one or two trials to avoid a white square from which it has received a shock. In birds there is a process of quick learning just after birth by which a young animal learns to react properly to members of its own species. Some feature of the earliest object seen can be imprinted upon the brain of the newly hatched chick and never thereafter forgotten. A German scientist, Dr. Heinroth, found that a young goose, freshly hatched, who saw the doctor before it saw any other goose, thereafter acted in every way as if Dr. Heinroth was a goose, following him around and so on. In this type of learning, therefore, a rather elaborate pattern must be printed somehow on the brain; this pattern thereafter acts as a model and moulds behaviour.

The way in which the system of rules is built up in the brain is also shown in the famous experiments of the Russian Professor Pavlov on what he called conditioned reflexes. By ringing a bell just before giving meat to a dog on several occasions Pavlov found that the bell alone soon came to produce a flow of saliva, which did not occur before. In further experiments it was found to be possible to use the method to train dogs to discriminate between two notes by giving meat after one note but not the other. If the difference between the notes was made too small the dogs became very excited and they refused to stand still and attend to the experiments as they usually did. Pavlov compared this condition with neurosis in man.

The doctrine that learning is all of a conditioned reflex type has had an immense vogue in Russia and is said to be a basic part of the theory of Soviet education. Like all systematizations it has some advantages over no systematization at all. But somehow we feel that Pavlov's analysis leaves out some essential feature of learning as it occurs in man, or at least man as we know him. Because of the limitation of his method, Pavlov actually took elaborate precautions to rule out the very phenomenon he should have studied. He did not include the random trial-and-error behaviour by which an animal or man searches for actions that shall produce satisfactory solutions for its needs. The Russian Government built him a wonderful laboratory with every room sound-proof and complicated arrangements to ensure that the dogs should stand quite still and be educated. With his outlook this seemed the right thing to do. It *was* the right thing to do to get that sort of result, but study by this method alone will not include the most useful forms of human behaviour.

If the attempt to show how patterns of action grow up in the brain has been successful, you may now, perhaps, begin to see how this is going to help us in the search for the nature of scientific inquiry. I hope to be able to show in later lectures that in this system of brain action lie clues for understanding the development of man as a communicating, family, social, religious, and scientific animal. At all stages we find first random behaviour, as we call it experiment or doubting. Then through observations of connexions between features that occur repeatedly, there is the recognition of similarities and recurrences, the establishment of laws, of certainty.

But we must notice that this process of replacing randomness by law may be a one-way, non-reversible process. The cortex of the new-born baby has perhaps few innate traits, it is in the main a blank sheet of possibilities. But the very fact that it becomes organized minute by minute, day by day, throughout the years, reduces progressively the number of possible alternative ways of action. Learning the laws of behaving in certain ways makes it increasingly difficult to learn others. We know surprisingly little about what determines the stability of the systems that get built up in our brains. They can certainly be to some extent reversed by new circumstances. We may forget, or learn new ways of speaking about the world. Some people manage to go on learning new ways much longer than others. Probably a part of their secret is that they constantly seek new circumstances. The temptation to go on relying only upon the rules already used year in year out is very strong. A really useful and interesting brain is always starting off on new ways. But it is a common experience that this gets more difficult as we grow older.

Every night when we are asleep we certainly receive some relief from our rules and wake up that much more alert and ready to observe in new ways. Within limits the longer we sleep the fresher we become. We do not know how far the unison beating of the nerve-cells during the night breaks up the patterns of action of the day. The basic patterns are probably laid down, as already described, in the sizes and connexions of the very fibres of the brain. These can perhaps also be changed, but only with some practice.

There seems to be a limit beyond which new patterns and new connexions are no longer easily formed. As we grow older the randomness of the brain becomes gradually used up. The brain ceases to be able to profit from experiment, it becomes set into patterns of laws. The well-established laws of a well-trained person may continue to be usefully applied to situations already experienced, though they fail to meet new ones. Here we see with startling clearness the basis of some of the most familiar features of human society, the adventure, subversiveness, inventiveness, and resource of the young; the informed and responsible wisdom of the old. At each stage of the development of our brains we have a special contribution to make, particularly if at each stage we realize that this is not the only stage: that doubt and certainty must be properly balanced.

In this lecture we have seen that each brain has to learn its rules of acting. It can then experiment with these rules, finding useful ways of modifying them. In man the brain rules are largely concerned with providing means of communication; we each learn the accepted way of communicating and this determines our view of the world. We also contribute to the evolution of the race if we improve that system and pass on ways of observing and describing that are a little more powerful than the ones we received. If it is true that each brain has a limited store of randomness, then clearly this process can only go on indefinitely for the race as a whole. To recognize the implications of this evolutionary process is perhaps to see a deeper meaning in the rhythm of birth and mortality.

Comment on the Third and Fourth Lectures

IN these two lectures I have tried to complete the presentation of how the nervous system works, and especially how it learns. The difficulty here has been different from that of the second lecture, which dealt mainly with the nature of nerve-impulses and reflex action. We have abundant information about those subjects and the problem was to present it in non-technical language. The problem in the third and fourth lectures was that study of the workings of the higher nervous centres has developed much less far; physiologists themselves have no generally accepted way of talking about how the learning process takes place. Many valuable observations on brain functioning have been made by clinicians and experimentalists, but they remain to a large extent isolated and not joined to form a satisfactorily coherent body of knowledge.

However, the fact that it is beginning to be possible to talk more fully about brain functioning is so important in its general implications that I have tried to put some of the ideas that are now being developed into non-technical language. A great deal of the 'science' that is described for the layman is so well accepted that the scientist himself is already bored by it. Part of the object of these lectures has been to show the uncertainties that arise as scientists venture to talk in ways to which they themselves are not yet fully accustomed. The thesis is that this extension of communication is often the prelude to entirely new discovery.

Those who study the brain are at present trying to find out how that organ functions to control our very elaborate behaviour. They start from the simple notions I have already explained—that the nervous system consists of a series of governors or regulators. Every time anything happens that

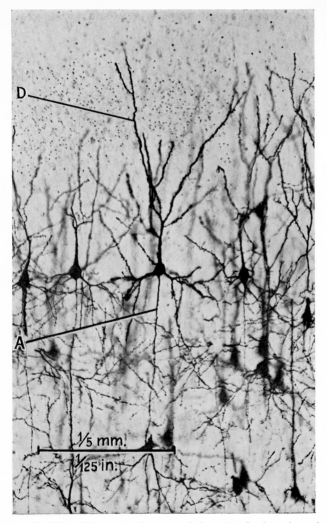

FIG. 10. Cells of the cerebral cortex of the cat stained to show the receiving dendrites (D) and the axons (A) along which the output is sent to other regions. The method of staining colours only a selection of the cells (about one in 50); if all those shown in Fig. 9 were fully stained the network would be very much more dense.

tends to upset the balance of the living system impulses are
sent to the brain and actions are set up that tend to restore
the balance. Examples of reflex actions that remove the
source of a change in the surroundings are familiar enough;
we brush away a fly, or quicken our heart-beat when we run.
On the other hand, the behaviour of, say, a writer at his desk
or a teacher in her class does not seem to follow the same
pattern as these simple reflex actions. Most of the interesting
things that human beings do seem at first sight not to conform to the pattern of simple responding to stimuli. Human
beings, as we put it, are not simply reactors: we say that they
act, they decide, and they exercise 'will'.

We can nevertheless apply the biologist's method to man
very much more fully than we have been accustomed to do.
Most of our actions are directed towards the maintenance
of the integrity of ourselves—especially if we interpret 'ourselves' widely enough. The difficulty in describing our
actions biologically comes from the fact that the brain uses
extremely indirect ways of ensuring this continuity. The
things that a new-born baby does are mostly of the type of
simple responses to stimuli. But the baby is also provided
in its cerebral cortex with an extremely plastic system for
learning complicated and indirect ways of behaving. The
cortex, after it has fully matured, ensures by a most elaborate
system of living that the balance of the organism is maintained. Even primitive man does not wait until he is stimulated by the sight or smell of food: he sets about obtaining
it, by hunting or agriculture, hours, days, or months ahead.
He uses indirect means such as observing the moon and
stars, sowing seeds, or undertaking all the elaborate procedure that is necessary to make a gun and shoot the prey.
Above all, in modern times he has acquired the habit of
getting a living by co-operating with others.

It would be easy to multiply examples of the indirect
means that we use to satisfy our needs. They seem to be so
far from reflex responses that nothing could be gained by
trying to speak of them in the biologist's language. This is

probably the attitude of most people today, because biologists have not shown that their way of talking is powerful enough to be useful for describing the actions of, say, philosophers, parsons, or physicists. Admittedly we are far from happy about our abilities; it is the attempt of these lectures to show that we can at least do a little more than is usually supposed.

An initial point that I hope was well established in the third and fourth lectures is that to an unsuspected extent our brain has to learn before we can even see things. Perhaps we hardly realize how as we grow up we acquire a set of rules that constitutes a way of life—a way of seeing, talking, and behaving, which we rely on for the satisfaction of our needs. It is a commonplace that we all have our habits of thought and action: do we appreciate the extent to which they control the whole of our life?

The biologist seeks to discover how these habits are built up and how the brain controls their performance. We are still far from being able to say clearly all that we should like about this, but what we can say is already useful in all sorts of fields, from surgery to education, psychology, and, I venture to say, philosophy and politics.

Perhaps the chief difficulty in speaking about the system that controls our actions is that the brain is such an active organ. Our ordinary language is framed for description of relatively simple sequences of events; we expect to be able to speak about the *cause* of each event in terms of what went immediately before. When we cannot see simple agents at work controlling a man's behaviour we invent them. For example, when we fail to follow in detail the connexions between his earlier history and some action we give up the attempt and say, 'it was his will', inventing the will because we are not competent to analyse the situation more fully. If we are to be able to understand and control ourselves better we have to be prepared to examine the actions of an extremely complicated system. We shall only be able to forecast its future if we look not merely for an immediate cause, but far into its past history. Moreover, our forecast will always be of its *probable* behaviour, not of exactly what it will do.

Some further details about the various parts of the brain and the way that they act may be helpful in achieving this end. The cortex is first and foremost the store of the rules that a person has learned from past experience. It fits the events that occur in the world around to these rules, producing some solution that shall ensure continuance of life. To perform this function the cortex has arrangements to receive input from the receptor organs and to send output to the muscles. In between these is the vast system of cells that constitutes the store of the rules and provides for the fitting-together process.

The input all reaches the cortex through a region known as the thalamus, which lies at the centre of the brain. Large numbers of nerve-fibres run to this region from the eyes, ears, and receptor organs in the skin. From the thalamus other fibres pass to receiving areas in the cortex, as shown in Fig. 9. Each of these fibres of course carries trains of nerve-impulses of the sort already described. When a pattern of light and shade falls on the retina, say the image of a circle, information is projected from the retina to the thalamus and from there on to an area of the cortex. It must be remembered that each nerve-fibre can convey only a simple sort of information—like a series of taps. But the whole system can convey complicated information, provided that the great number of simple pieces of information can be brought together. The cortex is so arranged as to make such bringing together possible, and it is worth while taking a somewhat closer look at how it does it.

The individual cells of the cortex are essentially like those already described in the spinal cord. They have receiving processes (dendrites) and an outgoing fibre or axon (Fig. 10). The fibres coming from the thalamus, which bring the input of information, end in complicated branches among the receiving dendrites of the cortical cells. Unfortunately, we know remarkably little about the details of the way these incoming fibres end. In Fig. 12 they are shown quite diagrammatically ending close to the dendrites of the cortical cells; a synaptic relationship similar to that provided by the knobs on the dendrites of cells of the spinal cord (p. 47). Such knobs have indeed been described in the cortex, but it is probably safest at present to regard the essence of cortical synapses as produced by the contact of the input fibres with the dendrites of the cells. Presumably the actions of the input fibres on the cortical cells are very like the actions of the fibres that reach the spinal cord, especially in that each cortical cell is influenced not by one but by many of the input fibres. This provides the essentials of the arrangement for collecting the information together. For example, impulses arriving from the retina along a number of widely separated fibres will activate only a few cortical cells, or none at all, so that no massive cortical process will be set up. But similar impulses coming along suitably grouped fibres will co-operate in starting off a number of cortical cells, which will initiate action in the cortex that ends, for example, in saying 'Give me that apple'.

Perhaps it is not too difficult to imagine how interaction is possible in this way, but it is hard indeed to follow all the details of the system. The cortical cells are arranged in layers, about 100 deep, and the receiving dendrites are interlaced in an elaborate way (Fig. 11). When a cell has been activated impulses are sent along its output nerve-fibre either to some nearby region or to a distant part of the cortex. For example, around the area to which information from the retina is projected there is another large area also concerned with vision (Fig. 9). Each point in the first receiving-field connects not with one but with *many* parts of this second visual area. And from there connexions reach sooner or later to many, perhaps all, parts of the cortex. The impulses arriving at any one point in the first visual cortex therefore have a chance in the second visual area, and subsequently, of interacting with messages coming in from other parts of the retina.

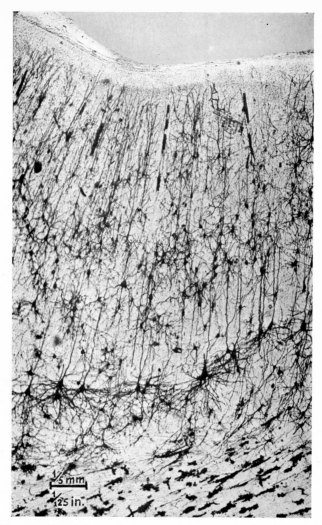

FIG. 11. Cells of the cerebral cortex of the cat stained as in Fig. 10, but shown with a smaller magnification. The interlacing network of receiving dendrites is well seen towards the inner side of the cortex, but would be 50 times more dense if all the cells were stained. The input fibres are not stained.

This is exactly the plan that we should expect if the brain is to be able to react not to simple flashes of light but to objects seen, as we say, as a whole. Clearly what we mean by saying that a person reacts to a pattern of light as a whole is that somehow the rays of light coming from all parts of it are enabled to interact. There must therefore be some mixing-place, as it were, in the brain where the effect of the light from each point can interact with that from others. We find this mixing-place in the second visual area. It may be that a great part of the secret of the brain's powers is the enormous opportunity provided for interaction between the effects of stimulating each part of the receiving fields. It is this provision of interacting-places or mixing-places that allows us to react to the world *as a whole* to much greater degree than most other animals can do. We have, that is to say, a machinery that allows for all the different influences impinging upon us to interact and thus to weigh up the situation. This is the great doubting machine, the machine for fitting together the parts of the sensory input at any one time and comparing them with previous inputs. For, in some way, previous experience has left its mark on the machine, giving it rules with which to operate, giving it its system of certainty, of law.

If the laws embedded in the wiring of the brain are efficient they will enable every sensory input that disturbs the rhythmic beating to be fitted into a pattern that will produce an effective output; that is to say, will make the muscles do something that will restore the system back to its steady state, the state that all organisms tend to preserve. To be able to understand all this more fully we should like to know much more about how the output of the cortex is controlled. Unfortunately the exact way in which the cortical output originates from the different parts of the great sheet of grey matter is still a matter of some dispute. Many long fibres arise from the strip running down the side of the head, above the ear, known as the motor cortex (p. 57). Fibres arising from this region certainly run to the motor

neurons of the spinal cord, the ones that control the movements of the muscles of arms, legs, tongue, and so on (see
p. 47). But there are also output fibres arising from many
other parts of the cortex, perhaps from all parts.

This account gives some idea of the basic plan and
arrangement of the brain. Each of the main input systems
has a similar projection plan, first to the thalamus and then
from there to some area of the brain. There is thus given, as
it were, a representation on the surface of the receiving parts
of the cortex of all the events that are influencing the surface
of the body. For example, when a point on the finger-tip is
touched, an appropriate part of the cortex becomes active
(Fig. 7). When a particular note sounds, impulses are set off
by the sensitive cells in the ear, and are transmitted, through
the thalamus, to a particular part of the auditory receptive
area. It is important to notice that the receiving systems that
have this cortical projection, those of the eyes, ears, and
organs of touch, are the very ones that we rely on to give us
our picture of the world of objects in space and time, the real
world as we call it. There are no true cortical areas for
smell, taste, pleasure, or pain. Smell is in a special position
because the part of the brain connected with it is very close
to the cortex; indeed the study of animal brains shows that
the cortex has grown as it were out of the smell brain. There
is still a definite smell cortex, but this has quite a different
plan of organization to the rest, and has a very simple
structure with relatively few nerve-cells. Man is an animal
that computes rather little with smells; they have a strong
effect on determining the general course of his behaviour,
as we say a strong emotional effect, but he does not use them
to determine the details of his behaviour. This all agrees
with the fact that the smell centres are connected with the
hypothalamus. We must not, however, dismiss smell as
unimportant. We have a mechanism that enables us
to discriminate by smell between a very large variety of
substances; also a smell may evoke a most complicated and particular set of thoughts and so must be con-

nected in some way with the memory system of the cortical computor.

We can learn much from these hints. Evidently the true cortical structure must be connected with the special types of computing that are appropriate to sight, hearing, and touch, producing especially the movements by which the animal or man learns to obtain a living. The method by which the computation is performed seems to depend on the fact that from each of the primary receptive cortical areas impulses are conducted first to a surrounding secondary or mixing area, where the exact arrangement corresponding to the body surface is lost. From these secondary areas there is then further conduction to many if not all parts, including to the motor cortex and other areas whose output controls the motor centres of the spinal cord. Each part is thus connected with the one ahead, as it were, in a chain from the outer world, through the sense organs and brain back to the world again through the muscles.

A significant point is that each part also has connexions in the reverse direction. Besides the fibres that carry impulses from the thalamus to the cortex there are others from the cortex to the thalamus (Fig. 9). The occipital cortex sends fibres to the area around it and this area sends fibres back to the occipital cortex. Probably the motor area, besides sending messages down to the muscles, also sends them back to the other parts of the cortex. And the muscles themselves contain sense organs of their own, which send messages up to the nervous system, recording how the muscles are acting upon the world.

We have seen already that this so-called feed-back plan runs through the whole organization of animals. It is the characteristic plan of regulators or governors, serving to keep the system in stable action. It is therefore very interesting to find it throughout the details of brain connexions.

This account gives an inkling of the layout of the whole thalamo-cortical system, enough perhaps at least to suggest that study of the brain is likely to be worth while and to tell us something of what goes on 'in our heads'. It must be emphasized that this is only a very rough outline. One might expect to learn that large numbers of people are at work finding out further details, at least as many as are working at the study of, say, gramophones or dyes. On the contrary, there may be about 100 serious and competent scientists in the whole world studying brain connexions. Yet there must be 100,000 or more chemists of similar competence. Everyone seems to feel that this is the right proportion; evidently we have learned to communicate usefully about the properties of matter but not about our brains. We can use our chemical knowledge as a tool to live by, but knowledge about the brain has only been of use so far in giving doctors and surgeons some notions of how to try to cure people. It may be that as we come to know how the brain operates this knowledge will become the most valuable of all tools, because it will tell us how to communicate better and thus to do everything else better. Already the first bold steps taken by doctors, working with only very partial theories, have revealed ways of restoring the function of communication to people who had become cut off from mankind.

It is possible, therefore, already to begin to see how the great sheet of cortical cells provides very large opportunities for the impulses arriving in each fibre, say from the eye, to interact not only with impulses from other parts of the eye but also with those in fibres from the ear, skin, and other sense organs. It is exactly by this means that the whole person is made able to react to the complicated pattern of information that is provided by so many nerve-fibres, each carrying its simple messages. The cortex provides most elaborate mixing-places in which opportunities are provided for interaction between the impulses brought by the millions of receptor fibres about the changes that are occurring at points all over the surface of the body.

That this is a correct interpretation of the significance of the cortical structure is shown by the fact that similar mixing-places are found in other animals that react to elaborate patterns of information. The octopus has a nervous system that has evolved independently of ours for more than 500 million years and has no thalamus or cortex or other such parts. Yet its brain provides opportunities for just this interaction, by which information is collected from the input of many fibres (Fig. 4). Two of the main receptor systems of the octopus are its eyes and the organs of touch in its eight arms. For each of these senses the octopus has a well-marked mixing-place, in the form of lobes whose characteristic is that the fibres in them run in a most elaborate arrangement of crossing bundles. This plan would obviously ensure that impulses arriving in any one fibre, say from one of the arms, have opportunities for interaction with impulses arriving from other arms. Because such interaction is possible the octopus is able to react to the shape of an object as a whole, rather than to make only simple withdrawals and other reflex actions.

Even more interesting is the fact that the octopus has a special lobe for mixing impulses coming from the eyes with those from the arms. In this lobe, also, most elaborate criss-crossing of fibres is found, and this presumably ensures that the octopus reacts not merely to the visual shape or tactile shape of an object but to a combination of the two.

Of course what we need most to know is exactly how the nerve-cells interact, in octopus or man, to produce the calculations. Here the government-office analogy obviously fails us. Can we do better by making comparison of the detailed workings of the brain with those of modern calculating machines? Such machines all work essentially as adding machines, because adding is a process that is easily performed mechanically, as the common cyclometer does it, for example. The giant calculating machines differ only in complexity. By working very quickly they make it possible to do multiplications and divisions (which are only really additions and subtractions) and many other sums of the same type. A machine that can do these things fast enough can perform some remarkable feats of forecasting, by working out the most probable result of a situation. We can say, if we like, that it almost seems to think. Yet as I mentioned in the second lecture, the biggest existing machines have only 23 thousand valves, whereas the brain cortex has 1,500 million cells. Can it be that the superiority of the brain is due only to this greater number? Some scientists believe that the brain works essentially like an adding machine, but we know too little to be able to say much that is definite about this yet. The essentials of the brain system seem to be (1) that it works with a very large number of units; (2) that each of them carries information of only a simple type; (3) that mixing-places are provided where the single channels converge; (4) that there is feed-back from every stage to the one before.

It is therefore certain that there are abundant opportunities for impulses in different nerve-fibres to interact in the cortex. It is reasonable to suppose that such interaction provides the basis for the very elaborate system of associating that is so characteristic of our activities. We learn to obtain a living by the use of indirect clues, which lead to the finding of food and meeting our other requirements. It was explained in the second lecture that the basis of the formation of this store of memory was probably to be found partly in the fact that there are opportunities for circles of action. These, it was suggested, maintain for a while any given pattern projected on the brain, so that ultimately it becomes as it were printed by an actual change in the brain cells.

This question of the nature of the memory trace is one of the most obscure and disputed in the whole of biology. The fact that there is such a trace is an integral part of the whole thesis throughout these lectures. It is this trace that determines the rules which control our behaviour. The difficulty we have in speaking about the nature of the memory store, perhaps more than anything else, makes it difficult for the non-biologist to understand our language.

Admittedly we still are not able to explain ourselves at all clearly, but we have good sound reasons for believing that both the cycles of activity and the printing on the brain really occur. It has already been mentioned that circular connexions are very common in the nervous system. Thus each receiving area in the cortex sends nerve-fibres to other parts of the cortex and fibres from these pass back to the receiving area.

It is significant that in the octopus, again, just that part of the nervous system that is concerned with learning is so connected up that the parts can activate each other in a circle. When the cycle is broken the octopus no longer remembers not to attack the white plate from which it has received a shock (p. 35).

However, for reasons explained in the second lecture it is difficult to believe that all memories are stored by the setting up of continuous circuits and we have to look for evidence that some feature of the nerve-fibres is permanently changed during learning. There may be changes in the tendency to discharge or some other characteristic of the cells, but of this we have little evidence. Professor Eccles and his colleagues in New Zealand have recently shown that if a receptor nerve-fibre is cut off from the surface, so that it carries no impulses for some weeks, then it partly loses its power to produce reflex actions. Other experiments suggest that such changes are due to alteration of the sizes of nerve fibres and cells, which are influenced by their functioning. It has long been known that nerve-cells deprived of their normal source of stimulation fade away and may disappear. To give one example, after loss of one of the eyes all the cells in the thalamus that were connected with it disappear. The converse is also probably true—nerve-cells that receive a great deal of stimulation become larger than those receiving less. Moreover, the size of cells and fibres depends also on whether they can deliver their impulses. This has been shown very clearly in the nerves of the limbs; if these are disconnected from their muscles they grow smaller, but recover again if the connexion is re-formed.

It is reasonable, therefore, to suppose that when two fibres are active together in the nervous system one or both of them will grow larger. If they grow larger they will grow nearer and hence the effect of each on the other will increase; synaptic resistance will be lowered. Imagine, for example, input fibres A, B, and C (Fig. 12) reaching the cortex close to the cortical cells shown diagrammatically by X and Y. Suppose that A and B are connected with points on one horizontal line in the retina whereas C is connected with another line. Now suppose that the animal or man was placed in such a situation that A and B were often stimulated together, or shortly after each other; for example, by living in a room with horizontal stripes on the wall. Assuming that at first impulses in two input fibres are necessary to fire either X or Y, it is clear that X will be stimulated the more often of the two. Therefore, according to the evidence given above, X will get bigger and will grow closer to A and B, which perhaps will themselves also get bigger. Both A and B may therefore come to be so closely associated with X that either of them *alone* can make it send impulses; certainly the probability of their doing so will be raised. What effect might this have? Suppose, further, that the nerve-fibre of X sends impulses, indirectly, to one of the muscles that move the eye horizontally, Y to one that moves it vertically. Clearly stimulation of any spot in the retina is now more likely to set into action a side-to-side eye movement than an up-and-down one. From having lived in an environment of horizontal lines, therefore, the brain has learned the rule of searching for horizontal lines. If we generalize such an effect over the whole eye, it would mean that all the cells such as X that produce sideways movements are more likely to be activated than the Y's and the person would then have a tendency to pick out horizontal lines.

It must be emphasized that we do not know for certain that such changes of cell and fibre size occur in the brain, but there is evidence that similar size changes occur in the nerves. Moreover, there are probably pathways such as XDX and YEY that provide self-re-exciting chains within the cortex. If these continue for a while after each excitation of A and

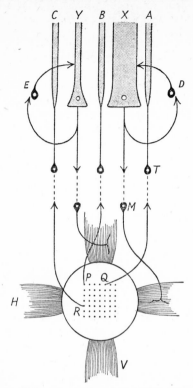

Fig. 12. Diagram to show the possible changes in the cortex during the process of learning. The cells of the retina are shown purely diagrammatically at P, Q and R with their pathways projecting through the thalamus at T to the cortex. A, B, and C are diagrammatic representations of the input to the cortex, coming close enough to cortical cells X and Y to stimulate them. From X and Y pathways lead back eventually to the motor cells M, leading to the muscles that move the eyes in horizontal directions, H, or vertical directions, V. If stimuli mostly occur in horizontal sequences PQ, then A and B will be active together more often than B and C, and X will therefore grow larger than Y, producing a tendency for the eye to move horizontally rather than vertically. See text, p. 84.

B they will further accentuate the tendencies of *X* to get larger. Finally, there is the fact that the cortical cells do differ very greatly in size. In most parts of the body the cells differ only rather little from the average. All liver cells, for instance, are rather alike. In the nervous system, however, though the cells all start similar they come to differ very widely, as Fig. 11 shows. This suggests that there is something specially significant about their sizes.

It is therefore not unplausible to put forward the hypothesis that the brain becomes actually modified or moulded so that it tends to react in certain ways in preference to others. Hebb, who has recently developed this hypothesis in some detail, expresses it by saying that repeated stimulation by any pattern of excitation sets up a closed system of excitation, which continues for a while and ultimately leaves a trace. This trace I propose to call the model or set of rules, which later determines the course of behaviour. The late K. Craik some years ago suggested that the brain functions by fitting its input against models. I suggest that we can now make this hypothesis more specific and try to find the models against which human activities are moulded.

This set of notions should not be too difficult to grasp. I have simplified it in order to make it acceptable without, I hope, exaggerating the evidence for it. It must be emphasized that we are so ignorant about the brain that we do not know properly how the input fibres are related to the cortical cells, and the arrangement shown in Fig. 12 is purely diagrammatic. The input fibres certainly do not end as simple rods as they are shown, but in an elaborate network of fibres interlacing with the dendrites. The suggestion is that the structure of this whole fabric of intertwined processes is literally altered by its activities, giving the wonderfully organized tissue that determines the way in which we act. It is certain that changes, however small, in such a delicate meshwork will affect the probablity of future action—producing for example, in the case shown, a tendency for the eyes to run from side to side rather than up and down.

There is one very severe difficulty that has not yet been mentioned. It is that when we recognize and name any object, say a circle, we do so whatever its size and at whatever angle it is seen. This is the phenomenon known as generalization. We recognize a figure or a face seen near to or far away and even when it has been greatly simplified, as in a cartoon. Animals also have this power, though not all to the same degree. A rat can, after training, distinguish a black triangle from a black circle whatever their sizes, and even if the triangle is upside down. The reaction cannot be therefore the simple fitting of a new input exactly with the model left by an old one. Some process of transformation takes place, so that figures seen at all sorts of angles and distances are correctly recognized and named.

Moreover, we know that the engram or model is not located in any particular piece of cortex. Professor Lashley has brought forward much evidence to show that in rats destruction of large areas does not result in loss of the ability to discriminate between, say, a triangle and a square. Quite large portions can be taken away from an adult animal or man with little or no loss of learned response and without impairing the power to learn again. On the other hand, it is very interesting that baby monkeys from which large areas have been removed, though showing little or no defect at first, prove to be unable to learn properly as they grow up. The same is probably true also in man. Evidently, therefore, the cortex provides a mass of tissue that is able to learn. Once the fundamental rules have been learned they can be applied, even by small parts of the tissue. Furthermore, discriminations that have been learned may be retained after numerous cuts have been made in various directions across the cortex. If the engram that was stored constituted a localized model, then it would surely be damaged by such cuts. There is evidence of the same sort for the brains of monkeys and men, and Boycott and I have found that a learnt response in an octopus is also not destroyed by numerous cuts.

These experiments show that the capacity to make a discrimination is generalized throughout considerable masses of tissue. They reinforce the conclusion that was reached from the fact that a circle or other object is recognized even when it is projected in different ways on the retina. This does not mean that the conception of a model set of rules is invalid, but it does mean that it is not a simple mould in exactly the sense of a shaped receptacle into which something is poured. We have to remember constantly that the cortex consists of vast numbers of cells and that their patterns of interaction are very imperfectly known to us. The learning process establishes certain relationships between cells, so that some types of output become more likely to occur than others. It is very much to be hoped that we shall quickly come to know more about the ways in which the cells become arranged to give us these rules. The evidence at present available suggests that it may be by increase in the sizes of sets of cells and fibres that are activated together, so that later activation of a few of them tends to excite that whole set rather than some other one. Pending further discoveries about the way these sets are arranged we can go on to see whether it is possible to give a useful account of human and animal behaviour on the assumption that it is dependent on the operation of rules of this sort in the nervous system. The remaining four lectures are an attempt to show how the development of family, social, religious, and scientific behaviour can be described in terms of the gradual acquisition of such rules by the individual, and their transmission from generation to generation.

Fifth Lecture

HOW WE LEARN TO COMMUNICATE

WHEN I was in Paris preparing these lectures I went one Sunday afternoon to the cathedral of Notre-Dame. As I looked up at the tremendous vertical lines of the nave I found that there were tears in my eyes. Why is it that one is sometimes moved in this way by a great church? When I left Notre-Dame I walked around the outside and looked at the mountain of stone, supported by its flying buttresses. Then, sitting in the sun, I speculated on this extraordinary human habit of making great buildings. As a biologist I naturally considered, first, what may be its significance for human survival, and, secondly, why do such works move us in this way?

I have been maintaining in earlier lectures that a special characteristic of modern man is the faculty of communication between individuals. I believe that it is possible to show that the symbols of society, such as churches, form a link in the process of ensuring communication. They play an essential part in establishing the rules of brain action that make co-operation possible. Our emotion when faced with them confirms the importance of communication in our lives. The symbol gives a sudden powerful reminder of our dependence upon others and elicits one of our earliest responses—crying. I want now to try to use these ideas to help in tracing the development of communication, both in the history of the race and in each individual person. In doing so I shall suggest one of the main reasons why these symbols of religion become the most important features of our lives.

Wild animals in nature mostly co-operate seldom; they usually react to each other by attack or by flight. Yet the earliest stages of communication were present before the coming of man. Reproduction involves co-operation between individuals of two sexes and in each sort of animal the males and females display particular signs that produce mating reactions in members of the opposite sex. For this end animals draw attention to themselves in most fantastic and complicated ways, from the wonderfully coloured feathers and the displays of birds to the evening dresses and dances of man. All of these demonstrations may be called sign stimuli: they constitute primitive means of communication. The intensity and vigour of our reactions to them perhaps result from their antiquity. For literally hundreds of millions of years our ancestors have reacted to such mating signs. It is not surprising that sex enters unexpectedly into so many aspects of our thoughts, speech, and actions. It is indeed the old Adam.

But in each individual person the mating reactions develop rather slowly. Before they are fully active the individual has already learned other ways of co-operating. The baby communicates with its mother with a cry and a smile; that is to say in the least sexual way imaginable. Later, the child gradually develops sexual reactions to other individuals. The non-sexual ways of communicating, especially by the use of words, have been acquired relatively recently in evolution, with the development of the cerebral cortex. But the sexual communicating system was already well developed millions of years before the calculating powers of the cortex had reached their present stage. The sexual system gradually comes into operation as a child matures and approaches puberty; it may not always fit easily into the rules that the cortex has been learning since earliest childhood. A result of the confusion may sometimes be the partial or complete failure of communication that we call neurosis. So with these ideas we can put sex in its right place as the earliest form of co-operation between individuals. This also suggests a biological setting for some of the recent great discoveries of psychiatry.

But what we especially want to know about are the characteristically human methods of communication. How does the brain make us speak, and therefore think, as we do? We can compare the use of the words we speak with that of tools and other indirect means of satisfying need. Even an ape will get food that is out of reach by dragging a box beneath and standing on it. He may make a pile of as many as four boxes. He can use a stick lying near the bars to pull food into his cage. He may join two bamboo sticks together for the purpose. These are examples of indirect solutions by the use of very simple tools.

There have been many speculations about the origin of language. I want to follow the simple suggestion that a name or a sentence functions as a tool to produce an appropriate reaction in another person. Sexual responses are produced by sign stimuli. For the non-sexual ways of communicating words and other signs are used in the same way. The words appropriate to each object, action, or situation are first learned by hearing them and uttering them. Each human brain learns a set of rules for producing words. It also learns to react appropriately to the word signs given by others. The brain must have such rules of operating, with them it selects those parts of the sensory input that are significant. A man born blind, on acquiring his sight, has to learn to pay attention to the outlines of things. He does this as a child does, by learning to select those features of the sensory input that have names. When children make drawings they tend to show only parts that they can name. In learning a language, therefore, a person not only gains the advantages of communication with his fellows, he also sharpens his own observation. This is a truism that follows from the fact that through the use of words men are able to use the observations of others. What it amounts to is that by the use of words we learn to see the connexions between things that are not obviously related to each other. In fact, like all tools, words lead to the satisfaction of needs in indirect ways.

The brain works by fitting the input that comes to it into the models it has already learned, and the use of words helps enormously in this process of fitting. With a word we extract certain features from any situation. Then, by using the same word again we can compare things seemingly unlike. To take a very simple example. We can compare an orange with the sun by holding the one up towards the other. But we can do it when neither is present by saying of each that it is 'round'. Then we can go on to discuss 'roundness', with all that it involves. The point is that words, besides making other people do things for us, also form a means of pursuing the brain habit of connecting things not obviously alike—of getting a living by indirect means. The whole recent history of the intellectual evolution of man has been a process of making wider and wider brain associations in this way. Man has been acquiring better and better models, so that he can fit together ever more and more experience. As a result, he can now understand, as we say, the cause of much that goes on around him. With this knowledge, properly used, he can take ever more courage from recognition of his own place in the scheme of things. Moreover, he can use this knowledge to do all sorts of practical things that once would have seemed miraculous.

The essence of the whole process is learning to conform to the conventions of the group in which the individual lives. When we ask a child to name something, we are teaching him to make a response that ensures communication. We are also passing on to him our own ways of observing. We have various means of rewarding him when he is right, punishing him when wrong. We can do it by feeding or beating him, but the first can only be infrequent and the second tends to cut off all connexion with him. We do it much more subtly by establishing first a special behaviour sequence, that of communication. The child's most important lesson is that the fitting of stimuli into a communicable form produces 'satisfactory' results. It is difficult to appreciate how deeply this first way of responding controls all the others, which are later learned through it. Once this is established it is not necessary to set up an elaborate appara-

tus of rewards and punishments to teach each new association. By giving the signs of approval or disapproval we can
show the child instantly whether he has produced the right
reactions or not. His whole brain system is trained so
that it seeks to organize all the sensory input into some
communicable output—to put it into words. From his
earliest days cutting off means hunger and cold, whereas
communication means satisfaction. The smile becomes the
symbol of completion and satisfaction and the cry that of
disorder and pain. By association with these signs that
communication has or has not been achieved, the names
that are 'right' are built into the brain system; the child
learns to select and observe 'correctly'.

It would be possible to follow out how the whole pattern
of a child's brain action is built up as successive rules are
learned, first in the family and then during social life. This
is the field of the psychologist, educationist, sociologist, and
anthropologist. The sequence is something like this. Early
on the child finds that there are rivals in the field, with whom
he must compete if his wants are to be satisfied. He uses his
growing talents of communication to attract the attention
that he needs, and even to prevent that attention being given
to others. Everyone who has been reared in or who has
reared a family knows how deep these influences are. A
complete psychological theory has been developed as to the
way in which position in the family influences the development of character. Thus as the child grows it develops its
methods of response to other members of its own species. In
a well-organized community these responses form a continuous series, so that by the time a person is adult he is a
well-trained social creature. This is achieved by carrying
over into adult life the practice of obtaining the satisfaction
of our needs by co-operation, a habit originally developed
only for the young.

It is not known what was the essence of the first social
invention, but a very important stage must have been the
development of communication to a point where it was

possible for large numbers of people to work in harmony. Remember that animals do not come together spontaneously; they usually tend to repel each other. If we modern men are different it is because we have been trained to react to particular sign stimuli, which serve as the means of bringing people together, of communicating. Each of the social species of animal has its own special way of doing this; dogs keep together by smell, ants by touch, bees by special forms of dance. In the case of man the cement for the formation of societies was already to hand from the use in family groups of facial expression and of speech. The individual depends on others for the satisfaction of his needs even in adult life. This is a relationship that in animals does not usually extend beyond childhood. Biologists have seen many other signs that adult men are like unborn apes. We have sparse hair, weak muscles, and thin bones of the skull. Moreover, sexual maturity is reached much later in man than in any ape. So it is no surprise to find in adult man behaviour that in apes occurs only in childhood.

The great new societies that grew up with the development of irrigation and other special forms of agriculture came to use some striking new means for keeping individuals together. By study of the remains left by these early civilizations, and by comparison with modern man, we can make a plausible reconstruction of how this came about. The methods that emerged were based on a continuation of the ways of brain action used by mammals for millions of years already. To find out what these methods were let us look at two of the characteristic actions of social man.

First, there is a tendency for large numbers to assemble together at one place. There is evidence of this from earliest times to the great crowds that gather today for rallies, congresses, processions, football matches, and many other events. Secondly, much effort is spent in building great structures within or around which these assemblies take place. The largest and most durable buildings that men make are not generally used mainly for the daily business of life, but are symbolic or religious. It is curious that biologists have paid so little attention to these two peculiar human characteristics. In no other animal is the habit of assembly quite so well developed as it is in man. The biological significance of the habit is that by it the brain associations necessary for communication are formed. Some of the earliest of these assemblies occurred at prominent hills of suitable shape, on and around which large numbers of people came together. One of the clearest pieces of evidence that we have about early social man is that he soon began to build large *artificial* hills. Objects nearly as big as anything that we build now were the product of some of the early agricultural communities, nearly 10,000 years ago. Such huge objects are found all over the world—an English example is Silbury Hill in Wiltshire.

I suggest that the value of building these objects was that they and their names were the signs by which men were trained to react to each other in such a way as to make society possible. At first, this must have been learned by all coming together at one place. Ritual feasting at such assemblies would indicate the satisfaction to be derived from association. Perhaps sacrificial ceremonies indicated the dangers of separation from the community—for this purpose, human sacrifice is no doubt best of all. Such ceremonies are occasions of training of the brains of the members of the community, so that they shall continue to react correctly, and hence get a living by co-operation and communication. Mankind has gone on assembling and building assembly places ever since. It is assuredly one of those features that the biologist should notice about him, that he tends to come together at intervals in huge swarms. Generally he puts on his finest clothes for the occasion and watches some display, whose symbolism often involves a struggle in which someone is victorious over someone else.

All sorts of other habits grew up around the central symbol of the hill. What more obvious, for instance, than to bury the dead in it, thus giving them eternity by placing them within the very sign of society? Indeed, this is a further reason why the sign itself must be large—it must include the past as well as the present. In fact there is a complicated relation between allaying people's anxiety about their future by burying the dead, and training their brains to co-operate while living. The two activities have been connected from such early times that we cannot say which came first.

The hill is a very convenient symbol because it is easy to ensure that the association is quickly formed. Everyone can stand or sit on the symbol while the ceremonies are performed. There have been, of course, many variants of the place of assembly; an early one is perhaps a huge stone circle such as Stonehenge, a symbol that everyone can get into. But there are obvious disadvantages about large symbols too. If they are to act as signs for the whole of a big population it soon becomes hardly possible to get every-one on or in. You can, however, have a lot of rather smaller objects or temples, in place of the original natural holy mountain. Their construction may be reckoned as the first act of making tools of communication, the direct ancestor of television engineering we might say. To be effective the places of worship must be alike and similar ceremonies must be performed at them, otherwise the association with the group is not reinforced.

A similar way of action may have led to other inventions of the same sort, namely still smaller symbols, such as images. These must also have standard form, and their significance is learned by exhibiting them in temples and naming them, after which they, or others of the same form, can be carried away and yet still preserve the associations. I need not pursue this subject here into its endless ramifications, but it is important to notice how use of one method of communication leads to another that is still more effi-cient for the purpose of reinforcing the association with the group. We shall find this alternation between new associa-tions and new inventions and new names proceeding con-tinuously up to the present day.

Thus places of assembly, or images connected with them, became the symbols of co-operation. These cruder manifestations of unity were the only cement by which, in early times, man the individual was associated with the group. He has come to find much more powerful methods later, but they are not quite so easy to use and the old methods survive for those who have not altogether mastered the new. Human brains, having learned to use the model of hill or temple, then proceeded to explore the possibility of further comparisons. We have seen that man speaks about himself by the use of a visual comparison, supposing that the special entity 'I' of which he wishes to talk lies inside the body, as a person lives in a room. This model was very early extended to all sorts of other objects, which were supposed to be tenanted by ghostly entities. It was obvious to apply it to the assembly hills or temples; each was given its own inhabitant. The essential feature of the assembly place was thus expressed by a comparison with a named person who lived in it, and the person in question was often considered to be like a father. The father was already the symbol not only of co-operation in the family, but also of the source of power, food, and the means of life generally. The model of a ghostly father resident in the temple therefore served to emphasize not only the unity of the group but also the value of the unity.

But here there is a difficulty; each temple has its own spirit. How then can all temples serve as a means of association for a large group? At some stage arose the habit of speaking of a single god, resident not in one but in many temples. This was a discovery of very great power. The peoples who first learned it produced one of the greatest of all human advances. Notice that it has the characteristic feature of many new comparisons; it seems at first quite illogical. The model stretches credulity so far that, like many new abstractions it seems on the face of it absurd. How could one person live in many places? An example of this was the dilemma of David when driven out of Israel to live among the Philistines. His god was associated with the particular soil from which he had been expelled, so he felt separated from his god and actually—and this is the point—he felt unable to worship him. Naaman overcame a similar difficulty by carrying two sacks of hallowed soil with him on a mule. But the real solution of the problem came by emphasis on the name of the god. I have already shown how, by naming, we abstract the feature that we want to emphasize in any situation. The worship of the name of one god, not associated with any particular place, was surely the symbol that provided the cement for the next stage of human evolution, in which we partly still are. It was a wonderful discovery, much more powerful than the use of visual symbols, which require giant hills, or temples, or images—though these had been great inventions in their time.

We can imagine how in this way modern religious and ethical systems have come into being and given great strength to the communities that have them. We do not know whether this development occurred once only or many times separately. In these lectures I am mainly concerned to trace the ways of human action that have led up to our present scientific age. For this purpose it is sufficient to notice that, in spite of the clues taken from Greek and Arab thought, science developed mainly out of the Christian communities worshipping one god. Ever since it has flourished chiefly in the more nearly monotheistic parts of the Christian world.

Before going on to describe the scientific ways of speaking that are current today it is important to say a word or two about symbols other than religious ones. Mankind uses symbols, especially words, at all levels in his daily life, to convey his wishes and intentions to others. I have been so interested to follow the use of the more central symbols that I have perhaps seemed to forget the innumerable humbler ones. It is the daily uses which are important and practical. The thesis is that the use of words to ensure co-operation is the essential biological feature of modern man, it is the way he gets his living. The general symbols of religion have had a special importance in this respect because they have been the cement that has kept society together. Another set of symbols that tends to do this arises round the use and exercise of the power that society wields—the symbolism of king and state. The symbols of religion and of power have much in common. The central ways of acting are the so-called theoretical ones, those of religion and pure science; the applications of these are the affairs of practical men and kings, of soldiers and engineers.

The purpose of this lecture has been to show how it is possible to use our knowledge of brain functioning to understand even the highest activities of man. Of course it has not been possible to make anything like a complete survey, but I hope that by these ways of speaking we can show the common factors that influence our behaviour in early childhood, as we grow and feel the influence of sex, and even in the development of our religion. By tracing the history of communication by the individual and by the race, one can see the continuity of the process of change, not only from childhood to old age but also from the earliest men to our present social system. At each stage the rules of communication control much of our observation as well as our action. Therefore we cannot fail to respect, promote and improve them, as rules. But by the same token we learn how to avoid their tyranny. Communication is important to us as a means, but it is not the end of existence.

Sixth Lecture

THE CHANGING SYMBOLS
OF SCIENCE

IT would be interesting to know how people would answer
if asked why they listen to scientific lectures. Perhaps
many would reply that they want to understand things
better, and feel that science can provide answers to many
of their questions. As a biologist, I should prefer to put it the
other way round, and to say that observation shows that year
by year more and more people are using scientific ways of
speaking and writing. The growing amount of science in
broadcast programmes shows the widening use of this
language.

To find out its advantages and limitations we may discuss
the development of scientific systems of communication
from the seventeenth century to the present day, describing
the actions of physicists and chemists in the language of a
biologist. What do these physical scientists do for man to
help him to get his living on earth? We shall find their
function to be very like that performed by those who, in
earlier times, provided symbols and tools that enabled man
to co-operate. As before, we shall find that as man uses new
physical tools his brain acquires new models or symbols.
Then, fitting its input to its new symbols, the brain makes
new observation possible, and produces a fresh output of
further tools. The cycle of doubt and certainty continues, in
science, as it did before.

The type of activity that we call scientific seemed to
develop rather suddenly in the seventeenth century. There
was a change then in men's habits of communication, and
new ways of observing and speaking about observations
were adopted. The rule with which brains had functioned
in the Western world in the Middle Ages was to describe

everything that was observed in terms of religious symbols. By this convention of speech and writing all human experience and action was unified. It was an efficient brain system, producing a well-organized society and reasonably stable conditions, which allowed for development of techniques and tools. Invention of new engines and forms of social organization proceeded, even though slowly. Each invention in turn provided new observations and fresh models, which served as means of discussing the observations. Thus, the inventions of mills for obtaining help from use of wind and water were important not only for the work that they did. In addition, by separating the doing of work from the action of living bodies, they made it possible to begin to speak about energy in a new way. Henceforth, change began to be considered not as something produced essentially by living things and by creatures like them, but as the result of an outside agent—energy. This way of speaking about change remains a central feature of science today. The developments that interest us most, however, were in methods of observation and communication. The inventions of printing, of clockwork, and of lenses were especially potent factors in the change in the ways of speaking and observing that led to the growth of science.

The invention of printing, during the fifteenth century, was a landmark in the history of human communication, and was crucial for the development of scientific behaviour. The act of publication plays an essential part in the procedure of science. The so-called 'true facts' with which traditional science deals are observations that can be made by anybody who has the necessary apparatus and skill. For the medieval type of brain making true statements depended on fitting sensory experience with the symbols of religion. Insistence on this correspondence ensured that all men agreed in their observations and all acted in the same way towards a common end. With the coming of printing it gradually became easier for people to achieve the same certainty about their communion with others by reading what those others said that they had observed. This was probably one of the main reasons for the changes that took place in the attitude to religious symbols. The Bible itself became the new symbol of communication.

As books became common men could look more directly at each other's observations, with a very great increase in the accuracy and content of the information conveyed. This is a theme that suggests a variety of trains of thought; the only one I shall follow now is the connexion between printing, measurement, and mathematics. Science consists in exact description of one's observations to other people. Therefore most of the exact sciences measure things—that is to say they compare them with some standard and express the result as a number. Measuring was a habit that was greatly extended in the seventeenth century, because numbers provide us with one of the best ways of sending a lot of information to a distance in a small book. There are other ways of doing it, say by drawing or photography, but scientists are probably right in making something of a fetish, a symbol, of measuring. The manipulation of numbers by mathematics was a further technique that was greatly improved in Europe at this time. As scientists developed the practice of measuring they continually developed new ways of relating the measurements by mathematics.

Almost as important for the origins of science as printing was the perfection of the clock. The accurate division of time into equal intervals was a characteristic feature of late medieval development. It spread from the regular life of the monasteries into commerce; until finally with the rise of industrial civilization the clock imposed itself as a burden upon man's labour. Today we are so used to speaking of time as an even flow that we find it difficult to remember that this is only a convention. Professor Evans-Pritchard reports that among the tribes of the Upper Nile time is reckoned by the needs of the cattle, milking time and so on, and the day is not divided into equal intervals of hours as with us. Seasons are reckoned from the migrations made necessary by the Nile floods. In our civilization the emphasis on a steady flow of time developed mainly with the invention of good clocks. This conception provided an important part of the framework of the new view of a material world that man created in the seventeenth century. Moreover, natural events were compared with clocks. The heavens and the human body were said to function like clockwork. In fact, use of this model was largely responsible for the practice of speaking of the 'working' of any system—a practice still deeply ingrained in us.

The new world of the seventeenth century, besides having a new time, also had a new space. The vision of this was made possible by the fresh information obtained with the use of glass and lenses. Lewis Mumford, among others, has pointed out the significance of the introduction of untinted glass windows in giving a freer view of the world and putting it in a frame. The Middle Ages used coloured glass to let light in, filtered through pictures of religious symbols. From the seventeenth century onwards men looked outwards through clear glass and saw a new world outside.

With improvement in glass manufacture lenses were made and used, at first for spectacles, which served to lengthen the reading life of the individual. But with telescopes and microscopes came the biggest shock of all, the sight of things that to the unaided eye simply are not there. Both instruments were discovered by Dutch opticians at the end of the sixteenth century and Galileo developed the telescope in the early seventeenth century. The motions of the planets that he saw with it could not be fitted into the idea that the sun goes round the earth. He therefore supported the seemingly ridiculous statement that the earth goes round the sun. The interpretation of astronomical observation that had been built up in the Middle Ages compared the universe with a series of spheres, carrying the heavenly bodies, with the earth at the centre. After Galileo's observations the whole model had to be abandoned. This was why the Church felt it necessary to make him recant.

The same sort of change came over other parts of science as reports of observations with the new instruments poured out. Description of earthly things had up to this time used the technique of describing 'matter' and its 'properties', a system we still largely use. It is often traced back to Aristotle, but is based essentially on the very ancient practice of speaking about anything as if it had some creature like a man inside it. In this language we might describe what a stone does when it falls by supposing it to be moved by a property of motion that we say 'resides' in it. Notice the significant word resides, suggesting comparison with a human house. If for each sort of observation we have to invent a new property we shall obviously soon have a great many of them, even for a simple body like a stone. We should have to describe also its properties of hardness, greyness, bitterness, noisiness, and many more. Obviously it would take a long time to communicate information in this way and that was why medieval science did not develop very far.

Galileo and his successors simplified the description of observation by ceasing to study only the properties of each particular body. Instead of talking about the power of movement of a stone as due to the property of motion within it, scientists now directed their attention to motion as such. They postulated a force acting upon the stone from outside. Remember that the use of mills had led to a new way of speaking about force. Galileo made another great change by altering the whole method of making observations. The simple way of studying a subject, say motion, is to look at it where it occurs naturally, in this case in men walking, leaves moving in the wind, or the sun in the sky. Galileo was not content with this. As Professor Dingle puts it, he took his experience in the form of experiment. He put spherical balls in grooves, watched them rolling down, and made measurements of their movements. This is the process that I call doubting. The medieval way of behaving was to describe only those things that could be talked about with certainty—

because they were like attributes of god. You used your rules to choose the right things to look at. Galileo's way was first to choose his vantage-point for looking—to set up an experiment as we say—and then to describe as simply as he could what he saw. By choosing carefully arranged experimental situations he was able to make observations that were repeatable. From these he tried to see new laws of the relations between things, so that he could forecast their behaviour. He made new laws from observations instead of only making observations from laws.

Science has found this system of isolation of certain sorts of observation from others to be an enormous help in producing simple, exact, and repeatable observations. It made possible the development of a special language for talking about each sort of observation—one set of terms for motion, another for light, another for chemical combination, and so on. Scientists have never been uninterested in trying to unify these different sorts of language; Newton, for example, tried hard to do it. But they have not made a fetish of uniformity. They have preferred to describe some things exactly, even at the expense of leaving out others. Scientists are united in their endeavours not by trying to force all observations into some preconceived system of law, but by insisting that the observations shall be freely available to all. Insistence upon this availability of knowledge is the central feature of the whole structure of science. It is, as it were, its central canon. It is important to notice that it contains the assumption that all people are equally able to observe. This is certainly not true, and therefore in defining science we must also define the varieties of man. I shall show later that this is not the unnecessary subtlety it may seem; in fact, consideration of it alters the whole structure. However, hitherto, scientists have certainly been very insistent about the free availability of their observations. Belief in this was expressed from earliest days in the growth of learned societies, devoted to discussion of the new discoveries. Such meetings have continued ever since and are active today. A biologist looking at scientists notes that each of them regards membership of learned societies as one of his most important activities. This is evidence that communication is an essential feature of science, as it was of the system in existence before. Publication and attendance at scientific meetings are as typical of the new behaviour as attendance at church is of religious behaviour.

The essence of the new method, then, was to pay attention to some features of a body—say, its motion—and to leave out all talk about other aspects, its colour and shape, its taste, its beauty, and its religious significance. The new science, therefore, seemed to many people, especially those in the ecclesiastical tradition, to be irrational and incomplete, indeed dull. So it was, and still is, except for certain purposes. The invention of the special scientific symbols and ways of observing, talking, and writing provides a means of communication that has great practical value. But it is only one of the possible means available to men. The tragedy has been that its relation to the others has not been recognized. Some scientists, therefore, have been led to make the mistake of thinking that their ways of observing and speaking were the only proper ways. This is to make the very same mistake that science itself taught us how to avoid in the seventeenth century. Scientific symbolism provides ways of describing observation to others. This is just what all forms of symbolism do. The painter has his own way of communicating his observations. Original painters find new ways of doing this, new art-forms. These literally enlarge the vision both of the artist himself and of those who look at his paintings. Artists have discovered new aspects of space with one symbolism, just as physicists have with another.

The fact that scientists began using a *variety* of symbols, without reference to one central set, is related to the general changes in society that occurred after the Middle Ages. What happened as these new verbal patterns developed was just what the biologist would expect: Western humanity began to split up into a series of separate groups. As a result gradually thereafter there was a series of new arrangements of the behaviour patterns of the larger groups of men, in the course of which, among other things, industrialism and modern nations were born. Since the new system looked away from man, and towards machines, it is not surprising that it neglected human values. This neglect is the chief practical defect of the systems of physical science. By a curious revenge it is now found to be also its chief theoretical deficiency—as I shall try to show presently. However, the varied new ways of acting did not produce the chaos in Western society that might have been feared. They provided new and better means of communication, so that men were bound into ever larger and more compact groups as a result of the very techniques that ignored the men.

What the seventeenth-century scientists discovered, there-fore, was the possibility of using new models and new signs for communication. Looking away from man, they began to form a picture or model of a completely new world, utterly strange to their predecessors. Space and time had hitherto been concepts considered purely relative to man and to god. By the use of the new exact ways of measuring time and distance the scientists built up a picture of a distinct world, the 'real' or 'material' world, as it came to be called, outside man and in a sense outside god, though the early scientists were devout and would have said that it was created by him. This is the world that we are apt to feel so sure 'exists' around us today: the plain, commonsense world of hard material facts, as some people would call it. What I am going to say is that the form we give to this world is a construct of our brains, using such observations as they have been able to make. Only in that sense does it exist. Before you give up trying to believe that this is true remember that our favourite 'real' world was only invented in the seventeenth century and that it then seemed very far from common-sensical to the average man.

Yet the new world invented by science was described in symbols not wholly different from those of the Middle Ages.

The new ways of talking were a mixture of old and new symbols, as they are in most periods. The scientists tried to abolish animism in their descriptions of their new world of matter, space, and time. They were only partly successful even in this, and in describing their own relation to that world they retained the old models almost unchanged. In a later lecture we shall consider the system that Descartes adopted of treating man as composed of an entity 'mind' set in another entity of a different sort, the 'body'. In considering the origins of physical science the point is that the adoption of this technique made it seem as if the situation was that there is a fixed district or region, the material world, outside us. The business of the scientist, if this is true, is to study and report on what happens in that world. I have shown already some reasons for believing that this is not a good description of the situation. In some sense we literally create the world we speak about. Therefore our physical science is not simply a set of reports about an outside world. It is also a report about ourselves and our relations to that world, whatever the latter may be like. Physicists themselves have come to recognize this and have found themselves forced to adopt principles, as they say, of relativity and indeterminacy. The point to grasp is that we cannot speak simply as if there is a world around us of which our senses give true information. In trying to speak about what the world is like we must remember all the time that what we see and what we say depends on what we have learned; we ourselves come into the process. This should make us much more humble in asserting that our present ways of speaking give a full revelation of what the world is like. As we expand our powers we should be able to observe and report more and more. This is what science has been gradually doing, and it has enormously enlarged our vision. We may take a few examples of this enlargement from the development of the sciences of chemistry and physics.

Chemistry was built up around the system that tried to describe its observations by saying that the world is made of something called matter, which can be divided into tiny pieces, or atoms. In the last century, chemists thought that they had found the indestructible atoms of which all matter is composed. We now see that this way of describing our observations is not adequate; we no longer speak of atoms as pieces of matter at all. The change has come about largely as a result of study of the phenomena known as electrical. The various events known as electrical discharges, lightning flashes, and electric currents occur under a variety of circumstances that all involve special positions of two or more bodies. For example, movement of a piece of wire between the poles of a magnet (the essentials of a dynamo) produces what we call a flow of current in the wire. Similarly, when certain chemicals are placed together in suitable ways, we have a battery, which also gives a current between its poles.

Notice the words we still use to speak about these new discoveries—'a current', 'flowing' (like water); a 'battery' sending out 'discharges' (like guns). For a long time the use of these primitive models made it difficult to relate our knowledge of electrical phenomena to others. Many people still feel the need to answer the question: 'What *is* electricity?' To ask that is to speak in terms of a primitive materialistic model. We have now learned how to avoid doing this. What we do instead is to find a language that will more directly describe our observations. In this case we say that electricity is the condition we observe when there are certain spatial relations between things—when a wire is moved near a magnet or when chemicals are properly arranged in a battery. We find that we can talk about electricity quite easily without asking what it is made of, or whether its flow is like water. In fact, provided we can accurately describe the conditions and relations in which electrical phenomena occur, we can do much better without the old models. The new method of description is by means of mathematics; we get rid of the materialist model and replace it by a mathematical one.

With the development of electrical tools it became possible

to make measurements of very large and very small quantities. The results of these measurements have given further evidence that our naïve way of talking about a world distinct from man and divisible into pieces of matter enduring in time is not adequate. This has produced, among other things, a surprising revelation of the extent to which physics in the nineteenth century had been using animistic ways of talking all unobserved. Physicists have been forced by their own data to a further extension of the principles laid down in the seventeenth century—namely, that the business of science is the simple description of observations, without postulating 'occult qualities', as Newton called them, as the causes of the observations. What are these further newly revealed occult qualities? Take the example of measuring. When I tell you that a stick is a foot long, I am saying essentially that I have taken a standard object, namely a foot rule, laid it alongside the stick, and found that they match. But do I simply tell you that I have done this? No, I say 'The stick has a "length" of one foot.' I interpose the occult quality, length, which I use as a model in my description of what I did. 'But how can that matter so much?' you might say. 'Surely we both understand what we mean by length, there is no harm in speaking in this way.'

It has been a great part of Einstein's contribution to show that there is a great deal of harm in this, that in fact our talking about such entities as length and velocity and motion deceives us into ignoring certain fundamental features of our methods of observation. For example, it leads us to suppose that the length of a body is independent of time and of where the body is in relation to ourselves, and of how it is moving. In practice it is found that this is very nearly true for ordinary terrestrial distances, but it is not true for very large or very small distances. We understand pretty well what we mean by speaking of the length of a stick on earth. We deceive ourselves if we suppose that the same assumptions apply when we try to measure the vast distances of the stars. However, Einstein showed that the way to avoid all such difficulties is not to speak of length, at all, but always to describe simply and exactly what the observer does when he is measuring and then to try to work out simple relations between the observations. That is why his theory is called that of relativity.

Something similar has happened as physicists have devised ways of measuring very small distances. It has been found no longer possible to use the old model of supposing that what was being done was to divide up something called matter into a series of bits, each with definite properties called size, weight, or position. Physicists do not now say that matter 'is made' of bodies called atoms, protons, electrons, and so on. What they have done is to give up the materialist method of describing their observations in terms of something made as by a human process of manufacture, like a cake. The word atom or electron is not used as the name of a piece. It is used as part of the description of the observations of physicists. It has no meaning except as used by people who know the experiments by which it is revealed. The results of these experiments are nothing more than relations between measurements, expressed in mathematical formulae. This may seem difficult to grasp, but we may consider that what has happened has been simply that with new instruments new observations have been made and then new ways have been invented for describing the results found with these instruments.

However, it is important to realize that great changes in ways of *ordinary* human speaking and acting are bound up with the adoption of new instruments. Some at least of the old animistic ways of speaking have been banished from the new language of science. We no longer speak of a world of matter, nor of particles, properties, or forces. Physics is no longer materialist. Instead it speaks of what we may call a man-world of observers and of the relations between them and the reports of what they observe. Since observers come into it a new phase is at hand in which a common science of physics and biology will be necessary. The models of each can

be used to help the other. Physical science has so far provided a most ingenious set of symbols for improving human
communication, and wonderful new tools have been produced as a result. The method has been powerful because it
freed man from the attempt to organize all communication
round one set of symbols only. Presumably the change
involved new ways of brain acting, though we can only
dimly see what these were. They involved adding to the old
linear, circular and animistic models the complicated ways
of brain action that we call mathematical. We may be able
to build a still more powerful science if we can fit the brain
actions of the physicist together with those of the biologist.
Science, like earlier human systems, has gradually changed
the use of its symbols and further changes surely lie ahead.

Comment on the Fifth and Sixth Lectures

IF we knew fully how the brain carries its rules we could identify those that are used by any particular person or at any epoch. We cannot yet go nearly so far as this, but by following the development of individuals and of societies we obtain some hints about the sort of rules that are involved. These two lectures attempt to do this, to justify the thesis that even our imperfect knowledge about the brain is useful for describing human behaviour. The fifth lecture follows some stages in the development of an individual in a modern Western community. The sixth lecture shows some of the stages in the evolution of human ways of speaking and behaving, as they are considered from the biologist's point of view.

The relationship between individual and racial development is a confusing problem that has led many scholars astray. The individual certainly does not learn his habits in the same sequence as they were discovered by his ancestors. There is, however, a special interest in the relationship between the rules in the brain of an individual and those in the brains of his contemporaries and predecessors. We acquire our bodily organization by inheritance from two parents; through them we are made part of the population that transmits and maintains the continuity of our type. The organization of each brain is 'inherited' not from two people but from a very much wider section of the same population. The survival of any population is made possible only by its gradual adjustment to change, which is produced in most animals and plants by selection from the variety that results from the unions of males and females. The facility of communication that man has acquired makes it possible to have brains that inherit their organization not merely from two but from hundreds of ancestors in the population. Human populations thus have far greater possibilities of changing their organization than are possessed by any other species.

History shows that man is in fact evolving very fast. The structure of most parts of the body changes only slowly, but the multiple influences that act on the structure of our brains produce continual alterations in our society and in the tools that we use for our life. It may well be that mankind is the most rapidly evolving of all animals, and as communication improves we may change faster and faster still. The many influences that control each brain make the whole race into a giant computing machine, serving to adjust the race to new environments and to maintain life where this was not possible before. There is a great deal to be gained from study of how this great machine works, that is to say how each individual learns his rules from society and conversely how the rules of societies change through the interactions of the individuals. These are the themes of the fifth and sixth lectures.

Our ignorance of the control of behaviour is so great that we still do not know how much we learn from others and how much we acquire by heredity from our parents. Investigations tend to show that we are mainly dependent on learning and that only the outline of our brain organization develops like that of the rest of the body by organic inheritance from our two parents alone. Very little of our behaviour is truly 'instinctive', if by that we mean determined only by the organic sort of heredity. For example, odd as it may seem, there is a sense in which we learn to be hungry. Hebb investigated this process in rats that had been kept on a low diet. When given food in a situation with which they were not familiar they would not touch it for a long time and became increasingly emaciated during the days that they took to learn that it was food. Rats presented with food for only a short time each day, say for 2 minutes, took many days to learn to eat for the whole of that time, which was still not long enough to enable them to maintain their weight. What we call hunger is not a simple stimulus coming from the stomach, it is an elaborate piece of behaviour occurring as part of the pattern of our daily lives. Everyone knows that if that pattern is disturbed we may fail to show the hunger behaviour. Similarly, 'appetite' in the presence of food is a learned reaction: puppies reared only on milk do not salivate when given meat. Particular likes and dislikes for food are probably all based on an elaborate system of learning in the past, and can therefore be changed in the future. An example of this is that people who go to live in a tropical climate have to learn to take extra salt to replace that lost in perspiration. Until they have learned this they do not understand the reason for the illness and disturbance that they feel, even after this has become quite severe.

Still more curious is the suggestion, developed again recently by Hebb, that we learn the reactions of pain and pleasure. We call anything painful or unpleasant if it disturbs the particular pattern and sequence of activity that has come to be characteristic of our life. In a baby hunger is one of the chief of such disturbances; when lacking food the baby shows signs that we should refer to in an adult as those of pain. Have we any reason for saying that in the baby there is any distinction between hunger and pain? The same signs are shown whatever it may be that breaks up the order of its life. There is much scattered evidence that the impulses discharged by various receptors produce a reaction that we call painful if they are disordered. People seeing light for the first time call it painful and shut their eyes again—the pattern of impulses does not fit with their brain actions. Bright lights and loud noises are painful.

Physiologists have been able to recognize certain receptors and the nerve-fibres connected with them as having the particular function of conducting pain. These pain receptors do not discharge impulses when the skin is lightly touched, but only when it is so distorted as to be in danger of damage. It is significant that the nerve-fibres connected with many of these receptors are very small and therefore conduct slowly. The suggestion is that they carry trains of nerve-impulses that arrive at the central nervous system in a disorderly way, that they upset the pattern of activity there and hence produce the behaviour that we call signs of pain. The body and brain seek every possible means of avoiding any situation that sets up those impulses, and special signs and sounds are given, calling the attention of others to the predicament.

The situations that we call painful or unpleasant are those in which we cannot fit the input of nerve-impulses to our set of rules. In the terminology of these lectures they are the situations of doubting or uncertainty. Since there is no fit we seek to make one by every sort of expedient we can devise, if only by ascribing the disorder to some agent that we call the 'pain' within us. By naming it we at least partly assimilate it to our life system. So we find ways of adjusting ourselves to every novel situation or idea, just as we seek postures or action that shall alleviate the source of the disruption that we call pain.

Because of the lack of definite pattern in the impulses that come along the small pain nerve-fibres, the brain does not easily acquire a pattern of action to which they will fit, as it does for the impulses from, say, the eyes. Indeed it is essential that it should not acquire a fixed action pattern if these pain impulses are to produce protective reactions against danger. They carry valuable information by the very fact of their disorder. But there is the interesting possibility that the brain *can* be trained to fit even these impulses. There is no reason why this should be impossible, particularly if special steps are taken to present them in as much patterned a form as possible. It may well be that this is the basis of the various exercises by which men teach themselves, as we put it, 'not to feel pain'. Pavlov showed that a dog soon ceased to show signs of pain when a given area of its skin was cut or burnt if food was given at the same time. If the stimulus was then given to some other area the pain reactions reappeared.

There is no reason why we should not explore scientifically

the best ways of learning to adapt ourselves to pain when necessary. At the same time we shall have to learn more ingenious ways of preventing our organization from being disrupted by damage and disease. Now that we begin to understand the brain we realize how it is possible for us to work what would formerly have been called miracles. But we can only do it satisfactorily if we are ready to accept change. We cannot do it by putting our faith only in old methods that have limited powers to remove pain and cure our ills. The 'miracle' is possible for those who take the trouble to learn new associations, to use new symbols.

It is interesting that the reactions that are usually considered to show pain are directed to attract the attention of other people. We cry out or make grimaces. These are reactions that we early learn to associate with disruptive influences. The baby cries when it is short of food, this being probably its inborn sign-call that attracts the mother. All situations involving disturbance of the bodily organization or failure of communication come to elicit the reaction of crying. Once again we see how deeply man is a social animal; his way of protecting himself against damage is to call the attention of others to the problem, and it is very difficult for other people to resist the call. The whole development of medical science shows the success of the co-operative method for preserving our lives—we can do far better together than we can alone.

Those who are not used to this terminology will object that writing about hunger and pain as learned reactions leaves out the 'feeling', which they will say is the 'real' pain. This is one of the points at which behaviourist language is often alleged to conflict with common sense, or at least to leave out the essentials of the matter. Certainly the nature of our subjective awareness of life presents a great problem: too great to be dealt with here. But simply to assert that what is left out is some*thing* called 'a feeling of pain' is to ignore all the lessons about the nature of communication. Anything that we can say about the situation called painful, any description we give of it, is part of our behaviour, directed in some way towards our conservation. If 'the pain' is what remains after all our description of it is over, then by definition we cannot talk about it. The function of language is to tell each other as much as possible that is useful, so that we may help each other to live. It is an absurdity to try to express the existence of something that cannot possibly be described.

Emphasis on 'the pain' as something personal, which cannot be described, is tantamount to admitting failure to tell each other enough about the situation to enable us jointly to meet it. This is after all exactly what is meant by someone who emphasizes that his pain is 'his own' and that it is 'real'—he means that he is going to keep it, because no one can do anything to stop it. Subjective language is defeatist —it amounts to giving up the hope of doing any more than saying 'There is some horrid "*thing*" in me breaking me up, and we can't stop it.' Objective language brings a great prospect of relief from this and similar puzzles and failures. It says: 'We have failed to find a way of preventing damage by this particular disruptive influence, because we have not yet succeeded in finding proper ways of describing it. We have been talking about your pain as if it was some horrid little demon sitting inside you. Let us now talk about it by comparison with machines and other objects, in terms of nerves and their impulses, and above all in terms of brains and the way they act. Then at least we *may* be able to teach ourselves not to feel pain and of course also to correct the disruptive processes that give rise to the situation we call painful.'

The behaviour that we call expressing pleasure is learned in a similar way. It is the behaviour that we show when we have succeeded in fitting the occurrences around us to the established rules of our life. One of its expressions is going to sleep, and it is significant that in sleep the electrical records show a rhythmical beating of the brain cells. Many cells are then acting together in unison, the brain is not using its calculating machine in the elaborate attempt to fit the input to its rules, because for the time being there is no more fitting to be done. We express the achievement of that state to each other by saying that it is pleasant, a phrase that we may use for the process of fitting itself when it is at least partly successful, as in some intellectual search. We also use it for the satisfaction of hunger or of sexual needs and, indeed, for going to sleep. When we say of a procedure that it is pleasant we mean that by acting in that way we find we can achieve continuity or certainty.

As in the case of pain, we have special communication signs to express this achievement of certainty. The baby smiles and laughs when it has been fed and these signs become the symbols of certainty, and especially of the achievement of communication. We laugh together when we agree, when we understand the same rules. A party is an occasion for such agreement; it is pleasant if everyone talks and shows that all share the same rules. One of the ways of emphasizing a common use of rules is to laugh at someone who does not share them—hence we laugh at mistakes, odd men out, freaks and Ugly Ducklings generally. Charles II laughed at his protégés in the Royal Society because they were trying to weigh air. The doubters, who are trying to find new rules, are always ridiculous, because they are not satisfied with the old ones. Jokes have the same origin, the fact that one sees the disguised or oblique point gives the assurance of understanding the rules of ability to communicate. Jokes about sex are the funniest of all, because they show an agreement about how to achieve the oldest form of communication.

To say that any situation is pleasant is therefore to indicate to someone else that a particular form of conduct has been found satisfactory. As in the case of pain, we have to deal with the argument of the subjectivist who claims that the 'real pleasure' is something personal and incapable of being shared. To describe any situation by saying that it gives pleasure, without further specification, is, as with 'pain', a confession of failure to describe it in adequate detail. If the quality and nature of pleasure is by definition incapable of description, then it is also not a subject for verbal discussion. Surely what we wish to do is to describe to each other as fully as possible those situations that we have found satisfactory. The danger of doing so by the metaphor of saying that they give some*thing* called pleasure is that we shall go on to suppose this pleasure to have other attributes of thingness. We may be led to ask what it *is*, forgetting that we have only been trying to describe our satisfaction by an analogy—by saying that it gives us 'pleasure', as a mother might give 'food'. Moreover, as with all such ways of talking, there is the fact that the analogy is an inefficient way of describing. To state that a situation is pleasant is only a vague description of the advantages one has found from it.

Of course, avoiding subjective language does not solve all problems; it leaves some severe metaphysical ones. Whatever they are, they cannot even be explored until one has fully recognized that language has the function of transferring information that is useful for living. Of course that does not mean that every word spoken is concerned with the search for food. Man's ways are very devious, and in our specialized society there are many individuals who contribute to the whole by the study of the means of communication itself—artists, writers, critics, and thinkers, for example. We can describe their activities also in objective language. The creative artist is an observer whose brain works in new ways, making it possible for him to convey information to others about matters that were not a subject for communication before. It is by search for means of communication that we sharpen our powers of observation. The discoveries of the artist and scientist are exactly alike in this respect. The advantage of describing these creative activities in objective language is that it tells us more about them and enables us to consider how to improve them. The thesis is that we shall be better able to train artists and scientists by study of the action of the brain than by talking only about some quality called their 'imagination'. It seems at first to many people that such language leaves out the 'feelings', which we all regard as the central feature of our being. Description of behaviour is thus often said to be incomplete, to omit the whole of psychology, and so on. This is a great mistake; objective language aims to leave out nothing that can be said, indeed it enables us to say much more than subjective language and animism allow. In particular it says that what we have called our pains and pleasures, assuming them to be in some way fixed entities, are in fact the imperfect ways we have learned for describing what hinders and helps our lives. By recognizing that pain and pleasure do not 'exist' we open up great possibilities for learning how to make life more smoothly continuous.

Not only do we learn to be hungry and to express pain and pleasure, we even have to learn how to learn. The special achievements of the human brain do not lie in speed of learning, but in the ability to select and react to complicated features of the input — to distinguish between slightly different shapes and sounds. It would be a very great gain if we could discover how the brain does this. There is good reason to believe that it is by virtue of the training it receives in methods of selection and naming of parts of the input. As we improve these methods we may be able to produce quite sensational advances in our powers. We cannot be sure of the limits in this respect, but I do not see why it is impossible to teach nearly everyone to follow complicated arguments and draw correct conclusions—even by the use of elaborate mathematical methods. The system we do learn for isolating and naming is complicated enough and yet we acquire it by very crude methods; our parents and teachers hardly know at all what they are doing as they teach us. What could we not achieve if we only understood more about this computing machine of ours and how to give it the rules best suited to realize the ends we desire? Already we can begin to speak about what it does; from this, from watching it develop and from comparing its action with that of animals, I see no reason why we should not 'break its code' and so learn to teach it very much better.

The difficulty at present is that we cannot see what form the rules take. In commenting on Lectures III and IV, I have explained the difficulties in the way of supposing that the brain contains actual moulds or models that depend on their spatial arrangements. Nevertheless, there is reason to think that some kind of anatomical organization is at the bottom of the secret. Study of the way the nerve-cells and their processes are related and connected seems to me to be one of the ways of trying to solve the problem. Perhaps that is only because I am an anatomist; the future alone can show whether this is right.

In so far as we can visualize the process of fitting input to the rules it seems to involve some kind of serial matching, in which as much as possible is fitted and what is left over is then fed back through the machine again. This idea is rather vague at present, but it derives from the fact that all regulative behaviour is like this—it is the way the engineer designs his steering mechanisms. The rudder is made to report back how far it is off course. Throughout the cortical systems there are elaborate arrangements by which the nerve-impulses flow on from one stage to the next, and then from that stage other impulses pass back to the first. We do not know enough about these pathways to be able to say how they make the fitting possible, but it may be by a kind of filtering out, at each stage, of whatever features of the input make a good fit.

To try to develop this theory in detail would be mere speculation. What we can do is to follow some of the stages in the achievement of the computor—how it comes to acquire its rules in each generation and how they develop in the race. Careful work on these lines should provide useful clues leading us to understand how the brain works. The fifth and sixth lectures are elementary attempts in this direction. They take me outside the field where I have any real technical knowledge. It is for psychologists and anthropologists to examine these matters, to analyse the patterns of human behaviour, and to show how they are produced by the brain. The only amplification that I can give now is to add some further tentative suggestions, nearly all dealing with methods of visual analysis.

Man shares with other higher vertebrates the basic power of reacting to isolated shapes in the visual field. There is no adequate theory as to how the brain accomplishes this isolation. We cannot say, therefore, exactly what gives man his special powers of reacting to many different objects, covering a wide range of sizes. However, the special reaction that we give is of course characteristically that of naming, and the learning of this habit by a whole society may well be at least part of the secret of how we store so much and such detailed information. The general lessons of the importance of communication and the symbols by which it is achieved are therefore also our chief lessons of observation. Those who cannot use mathematics are disqualified for 'observing' electrons.

One of the first lessons that a baby learns with its eyes is to focus and move them together, and to follow along lines, especially continuous lines that cause an object to stand out from its background. The objects that are picked out earliest are those that have special significance for the life of the child, for instance its mother's face. Certain patterns seem to be especially easily reacted to, in particular circles. Some time after the child has acquired the power to react to objects it begins to name them. It is taught to put them in the 'right' categories by its successes and failures in communication. This habit of saying what things *are* is certainly such a deep-seated one that we come to ascribe special importance to placing entities in the 'right' category, as is indeed necessary if communication is to proceed satisfactorily.

The earlier stages of communication about visual information are therefore accomplished by the rule of comparing any new input with the engram corresponding to certain shapes that have acquired significance. The name of which-ever of these fits best is thus used to describe the unknown. There is a strong tendency to insist on the possibility of treating all the input in this way, that is to say by dividing it up into entities that can be suitably named, so that their actions will be described. Everyone knows the persistent attempts of children at certain ages to give names to every-thing. The results may be ludicrous, but the child very much resents being laughed at when it makes a mistake in identi-fication. This habit of classification is thus the basis for our insistence on a rule of law, which acquires outstanding impor-tance in the course of racial and individual development. The input cannot be left as a chaos; it must be sorted, ordered, and named, and somehow made consonant with our plan of life.

Living things, and particularly living people, are the pre-dominant features of the environment, and a very common way of describing any action is by postulating some agent like a person, which is responsible for occurrence and occupies the region where the action occurs. There are end-less familiar examples of this tendency to use the model of a human being as a means of description. A whole family of them is used to describe each person himself by referring to various hypothetical agents, the self, ego, mind, soul, will, and so on, which are presumed to be resident within the body. The structure of words used by medicine in the Middle Ages provides many examples and they are discussed in the comment on the seventh lecture.

The classification of the host of models used for descrip-tion in daily life would of course be a tremendous task and we have no really clear indications of how this could be done in any systematic way. Nevertheless there is no need to be defeatist about it. It may be easier than we suppose to find out the way we use the brain. Underlying the immense multiplicity of our actions and symbols there are probably common patterns, if we are clever enough to see them. The following of lines and circles is certainly at the bottom of our reading habits. We somehow learn to group together whole sets of lines or curves and thus quickly to extract the information from the page. Any unfamiliar mixturE of linEs and curvEs will brEak up thE habit; for ExamplE, print in which all thE e's are writtEn capital E's is almost unrEadablE—onE cErtainly cannot skim through it quickly.

There is, as yet, very little information about the way in which the powers of the eyes and visual brain centres affect the speech centres and vice versa. There is evidently an elaborately interwoven system, in which the sorts of patterns that the eyes and the brain have been selecting come to be associated with the patterns that the ears and brain have been selecting and with the sounds that the brain and tongue have been producing. It should not be beyond our powers to learn about the way that this pattern of action has been developed in the brains of the past and is taught to those of the present.

Probably the whole system at any stage has certain general characteristics that affect all its manifestations. We are all familiar with fashions of dress, each seeming to be 'natural' at the time, but looking very queer even ten years later or less. Similarly, there are certainly fashions of ways of seeing in general, and these are reflected in art forms of all sorts. Wholly different representations were acceptable to the eye in, shall we say, the thirteenth, fifteenth, seventeenth, and twentieth centuries in western Europe; the conventions of India, China, and Japan are different again from all of these.

These facts are familiar enough; what we have not succeeded in doing is to extract the essential ways of operating that are characteristic of each fashion. When we try to do it the attempt is found to be imperfect, but perhaps it is worth while as a stimulus to do better. In the Middle Ages the usual way of brain operating was visual and classificatory, using the logic of Aristotle and the models of the Church. Many of us are still trained in this way although it is a very handicapping one, because it teaches us to divide all our observations into rigidly separate and sharply defined categories and to leave our description when at the level of saying what some phenomenon *is*, often by use of an animistic comparison.

The early scientists, as I have explained in the sixth lecture, gradually broke away from these habits and acquired the practice of reporting observations more fully by comparison with human tools. Their reaction from animism was to say that everything was to be described in terms of 'matter', whose actions, like those of our man-made machines, could be completely forecasted. So grew up the fashion of scientific materialistic determinism. It was very successful in the technical fields, but it never provided a language that was generally used in everyday life. Its own symbols were those of the classical Newtonian dynamics, but it failed to make these as useful for daily communication as the old logical system, perhaps because it studied power problems and not the communication problem as such.

As information was collected new scientific methods and fashions succeeded each other, especially with the development of knowledge of electrical phenomena. The verbal habits of materialism have now been abandoned for purposes of exact scientific communication. Instead of directing attention to the separation of matter into distinct parts we now deal in the study of relations between observations, and of the organization that they reveal. The methods used are those of statistical mechanics and wave mechanics, a symbolism that is available as yet only to very few.

The production of new ways of speaking and new symbols has certainly developed faster than our knowledge of how these methods of communications are acquired and can be taught. This is a dangerous situation, because it leaves us with a relatively small number of individuals provided with greater skills than the others, but unable to say exactly how they have acquired these skills. For this reason alone it is very important to try to find out how the brain works at each stage. The lectures suggest some of the ways in which the symbols of religion and science and the tools that man makes came to be used for the purpose of making comparisons. I have perhaps not sufficiently emphasized the very great importance of written words and other symbols. Very little is known about the way the brain stores its memory of these or how fitting to them is performed in reading. Each group of signs comes to stand for some particular sensory input, so that when we see the word or set of words a whole complex of brain processes is activated. Reading thus enables the life of others to be lived, as it were, in the brain, with very little effort. We can share the observations of others in their absence. Particularly important of course is the opportunity this gives for each of us to experience a vastly wider range of situations than we could possibly do in a lifetime in the ordinary way.

As we learn more of brain processes it should be possible to increase very much the amount of information that can be conveyed in this way. Our methods of teaching to read and to use chemical and mathematical symbolism are at present quite empirical and are clearly of only limited effectiveness. As we come to know more in detail what we are doing we should be able to make the content of our written language very much fuller, and more quickly and widely learned. The possibilities of improved co-operation produced in this way may be very great. There is no obvious reason why a large proportion of the population should not read pages of mathematical symbols as readily as they now read print. By this means we could come to explain all the complexities of life more fully to each other, and therefore become correspondingly better at co-operation.

The differences that are seen at present between adults in their powers of logical reasoning and the handling of symbols give the impression that there may be profound genetical differences in our powers for such tasks. No doubt there are such hereditary differences, but we have little reliable information about the extent to which they contribute to the differences found between the adults. Much of the learning of the general rules of behaviour goes on so early in life that we have few studies to show whether babies differ in aptitude for it. Intelligence tests administered later certainly do not test the powers of the untrained brain. It would be very valuable indeed to have methods for measuring the power of learning to learn, of acquiring general rules and applying them. It is difficult to see how this could be tested, however, except in the very young. As we have seen, the brain we inherit physically from our parents may be largely a blank sheet of possibilities; as it acquires an organization by social inheritance its powers rapidly become altered. It may be that for practical purposes what we call the innate powers of a person, acquired at birth, are less important than is usually implied. What is important in a schoolchild or man is what he can do with the organization he has acquired by the joint operations of physical and social inheritance. The problem of what he might have done with a different training is of interest to the educational researcher but not to his fellow men, who have to live with him as he is. There certainly are differences in learning powers inherited from our parents, but until we know how the brain works and what these differences are it is impossible to say whether they could be overcome.

This brings us to the fascinating question of how far later education can compensate for lack of early training in providing a general system of rules that will allow us to use any particular form of symbolism. Can an older person learn how to learn from experience and especially how to modify and improve his use of symbols? Certainly it becomes harder for an old dog to learn new tricks, but when we know more about the processes involved I see no reason why we should not be more successful in this respect than at present. Surprisingly few people have the power to learn new symbolism, even after expensive schooling, and it is difficult to believe that the methods we use to teach this are the best possible. Among undergraduates there are not many who are able to do more than acquire information by attaching it to the system of concepts they have been taught:

only rarely are they able to examine these concepts. No one has devised any general system for teaching the power to use new sets of symbols; most science students, for example, show a blank incomprehension of any system of speech except that involving simple visual, animistic, and material- istic terms. Yet the English secondary school system is prob- ably nearly or quite the best in the world in these respects, and the type of brain we produce is especially pliable and able to be used in various situations.

There is no doubt that schooling, even relatively late in life, strongly influences the brain, but we have a long way to go to find how best to use the time available for teaching. Yet there is much criticism of educational pioneers who try to investigate these matters and to find new methods. Especially in the universities there are many who say that education is in some mysterious way a sort of automatic process and that there is little need to pause to think what can and should be taught. Certainly the methods that each generation of teachers learns from the one before should not lightly be changed. Many unexpected complications arise with any new form of teaching. But with more careful study and more daring in exploring new methods I believe that we could strikingly improve our power to train brains to convey information to each other. No other avenue holds so much hope for improvement in the welfare of the human race.

Seventh Lecture

THE MECHANISTIC INTERPRETATION
OF LIFE

THROUGHOUT these lectures I have been speaking the language of a biologist. This is the way my brain has been trained to work—these are the words its rules produce. It is, of course, only one way of approaching the problems of life. Other people's brains work differently, and it is not for me to say which is the best way. I do believe, however, that there are some peculiar advantages in the biological method. By studying all the variety of life, including the life of man, biologists can include and transcend the other sciences. Moreover by their emphasis on the continuity of life they give us some bearings to show us our position in relation to the past and the future.

In order to try to bring out the characteristics of the biological method I propose in this lecture to use it to study biologists themselves. The thesis is that the value to the race of religious and scientific symbolism is to ensure co-operation. Advances are made by the doubters, who suggest new comparisons, which produce better communication. What comparisons does the biologist use and how have they improved through the centuries? One of the most obvious ways of speaking about plants, animals, and men is to assume that they can be investigated by dividing into parts. The supposition that the body 'is made' of a number of entities or 'parts' that can be revealed by dissection is so obvious that most of us cannot get away from it even now. We feel that it is natural that if we cut up a body and look inside it we shall find what is 'really' there. Of course there is a sense in which this is true. Man is a creature who makes special use of the information that he gets with his eyes. If he divides up complicated systems, such as living bodies, he will find parts inside to talk to his fellow men about. I am an anatomist by profession and should be the last to deny this. What I want to criticize is the idea that by dividing and dividing one will ultimately find in some way the real or true unit, which gives full knowledge of the body. This is an outmoded materialism, which still lingers in many people. Physical scientists thought for a long time that they could manage by speaking about atoms in this way and they did indeed get useful results, but they are obtaining even more exciting ones now that they have abandoned it. Similarly, we biologists have made great progress on atomistic lines, but we shall now make more still if we can bring ourselves to modify them.

Let us look first at the parts we can find. A convenient single unit to be found in nearly all living things is the cell. The dissecting tool that revealed it was the microscope. The human body contains more than a million million cells, each less than one-thousandth of an inch across. Every cell contains a central round body, the nucleus, made of some material that differs from the rest. Inside the nucleus are still smaller bodies, the chromosomes. The nucleus contains a fixed number of these in each sort of animal. Human beings have twenty-four pairs of them. They are the carriers of heredity. Each egg and spermatozoon has only half the adult number and when egg and sperm fuse in the union of male and female the full number is restored. So you get half your chromosomes from your mother, the other half from your father. It is by means of the chromosomes that hereditary characteristics are passed on. Each of them carries a number of genes, the hereditary determinants. The fact that many combinations of chromosomes are possible makes it unlikely that any two individuals in a population will be identical. This shows us at once the value of the sexual method of reproduction to the race. It mixes up the genes of pairs of people in a random way: in fact it ensures that we shall not be all alike. Moreover, the genes themselves alter from time to time by a change in the chromosomes known as mutation. This change also happens in a random manner, but is speeded up by radiations, such as X-rays, or those emanating from explosion of an atom bomb. Geneticists, the people who study inheritance, have to work out the chances that particular combinations of chromosomes will occur. In this way they can, in suitable cases, forecast the probability that any given child will, for example, have blue or dark eyes. It is seldom that they can make an exact forecast about any one child, but they can give the odds that it will be of one type or another (see p. 148).

Biologists have had to make a careful study of the subject of chance. The physical scientists, from Galileo onwards, have tried to find, as we say, the causes of happenings. They arrange experiments in which everything is made as simple as possible, and then find out how one single change will influence the result. This is an extremely useful method for disentangling the different influences that affect any process. But events in nature are usually influenced not by one but by a large number of different agencies. The combined action of many small influences produces what we call chance. Biologists also make experiments, but they cannot simplify things enough to be able to forecast *exactly* what will happen. The study of inheritance and of populations has therefore led to the development of special mathematical methods for forecasting probabilities—a branch of statistics.

Can we say, then, that the original hope of defining life by study of parts within the body has been fulfilled? The microscopist has succeeded in finding visible bodies, the chromosomes, which determine hereditary characters. This is certainly very satisfactory so far as it goes. Yet to say that we resemble our parents because we inherit some twenty-four minute dark-coloured rods from each of them is not enough. However enthusiastic one may be as an anatomist and microscopist, it is difficult to feel that by dividing and naming *alone* one reaches the last word that can be said about living things; one tries also to say what things are made of and how they act. Ever since the sixteenth century another group of scientists, the physiologists, has been at work describing man, animals, and plants by means of a different set of words. Before that time biologists spoke about the actions of the body as if each part had qualities like those of a living creature. Thus, the gall-bladder was said to be friendly and attracted the yellow bile, which was supposed to correspond to fire and gave liveliness to the temperament. Three sorts of spirits, natural, vital and animal, were said to control the bodily operations. The idea of spirits came from that of vapours—for example those of alcohol, which are invisible and yet able to produce effects. The spirits formed a half-way house between bodily events and the controlling soul. Comparison with them was thus an attempt to bridge the gap between mind and matter that arose from describing man as a material body occupied by an immaterial mind. This all seems very primitive to us, but we can see how the system worked. In order to be able to talk and write about the actions of the body man must compare them with something; the most obvious comparison is with the sources of action and change that we know best, namely ourselves and the tools we use.

The actions of the nervous system were the hardest of all to speak about. The movements of the muscles and limbs were supposed by the sixteenth-century physiologists to be produced by the will of the anima or soul, which resided in the whole body. The brain was the place for refining the animal spirits, leaving ultimately reason, which is free from earthiness and thus able to think, to will, and to survive the body. Notice, once again, the use of analogy, taken this time from the process of extraction of metals.

Descartes began the analysis of the functions of the nervous system by making the comparison with a machine, say a clock, wound up to go and triggered off by stimuli in the outside world. This left us with the method of speaking about the nervous system in terms of stimulus, sense organ, impulses conducted along nerves to the brain and thence back again to make the muscles work. It is a scheme we all use daily, but as we have seen in earlier lectures it does not take us as far as we should like with talking about what goes on in the brain. Descartes himself got over the difficulty by the use of the very device that he was repudiating. The essence of his new system was to show that each part of the body acts as it does for 'mechanical' reasons and not because it contains some occult spirit or faculty disposing it so to act. There was, however, a long tradition that the soul controls the action of the brain by operating on the pineal gland, which was supposed to regulate the flow of spirits between the cavities of the brain. Descartes did not invent this view but he developed it, supposing that the valve could be operated either by the flow of spirits inwards from the sense organs, that is, as we should say, reflexly, or by the will. In doing this, therefore, he carried over directly the medieval system. He made possible the acceptance of much that was new by keeping the old system to speak about the most difficult part.

The model of the body as a machine has been the basis of much of the most useful part of our biology. With it we can find out how the body 'works', how much food must be supplied to provide the fuel, and so on. In fact the machine model is the basis of much of agriculture and medicine. However chemistry, as it expanded during the nineteenth century, provided very powerful new models for living activities. The practice of saying that living things are in some sense made of the same stuff as non-living ones is in itself a very original one. In most ways the two sorts appear obviously different. It is not easy to see that there is any sense in saying that the body is made largely of carbon, like coal, and oxygen and nitrogen like air. It would be easy to make out that it is a ridiculous and silly thing to say. However in the nineteenth century it was shown that it is possible to isolate from the body elements, such as oxygen, that are indistinguishable from those found in the non-living world. Moreover, it is also possible to make in the laboratory, using only non-living materials, some at least of the substances that are found in living bodies. So the great science of bio-chemistry began and is still rapidly expanding. Biochemists are often asked the question whether, if they knew a little more about the details, they would be able to 'explain' life fully in terms of chemistry. Some of them reply that they believe that they could do so. One admires the courage and persistence implicit in this hope, for living chemistry is very complicated. But perhaps it would be wise to consider care-fully what might be meant by 'explain'. No doubt great progress will be made by use of current ways of speaking, but the changes in the use of symbols through the centuries suggest that the questioner and the biochemist were being too simple minded in asking and answering such a question. No doubt man in the future will be able to say much more inter-esting and useful things about living creatures than he can now—but they will be in terms as different in content from those of today as electron is from angel. The use of symbols grows gradually. It is not easy for each generation to realize that the names it uses have a past history and that the con-cepts used in the future will be very different from those of today.

When we come to look closely at the chemical inter-changes between the body and the environment we find that the body does not maintain a static structure, as the com-parison with a machine suggests. Oxygen passes into the body, is burned, and is breathed out again as carbon dioxide. Was that oxygen ever part of the living body? Probably many people would say that it has merely passed through and been used by the body. But the paradox is that if one says this one will find that there is no enduring body at all. For we now know that even the apparently most stable parts, such as the bones, do not remain always compounded of the same actual molecules. If living things consist of no steady fabric of stuff but are continually changing, what is it then that is preserved? What is it about the chromosomes that makes them the bearers of heredity? What is it that makes each life in some sense the same from year to year?

Individual chemical atoms remain in the cells for only a short time; what is preserved must be the pattern in which all these interchanging atoms are involved. 'Pattern', you may say, 'what do you mean by that? Are you comparing me with a carpet?' That is just the trouble—we find it hard to find a proper model. Living patterns are not stable like those of pictures or carpets. A whirlpool might be a better simple analogy—the pattern of swirls in a river. The matter of these is continually changing and yet there is a sense in which each swirl remains the same. We might say that the flow through them is organized in a particular way. 'Yes, but organized by what or by whom?' In the case of the river it is by the historical events of the past, which have left a certain arrangement, so that the water must flow through making just those patterns and swirls. So, in the case of the body, the organization is such that the matter must flow through in certain ways.

Biology, like physics, has ceased to be materialist. Its basic unit is a non-material entity, namely an organization. But the organization is vastly more complicated than that of any river. It is kept in certain channels by the environment, acting in a sense as do the banks. If a stream stops, the banks remain, and therefore a river that has dried up may form again the same patterns. But the living patterns are so complicated that they are kept intact *only* by their continued activity. If they stop they are never restarted. The living patterns have developed a wonderful permanence none the less. They have the characteristic that every time there is any change in the banks the swirls make a compensating change and thus keep intact. The river analogy begins to fail us here and we may return instead to quite a different one. If we want to understand an elaborate organization such as the body we may find it useful to compare it with an organization that we do understand. In an earlier lecture I compared the brain with a vast office devoted to keeping itself intact. I shall not press the analogy again here, but development of the study of human organizations is beginning to provide us with powerful models for comparison with our own bodies. As sociology and the study of human organizations develop we are likely to find their terms useful in the very hard task of describing the living body, for which at present we have no proper model. The study of large populations and how they behave is one of the most recent human techniques. We now have methods of finding out what people do, by questionnaires, samples, market research, and other techniques, and statistics has a new set of symbols and methods of observation. These may help us greatly in studying the body, which is after all described as well by saying that it is a population of cells and chemical molecules as by comparing it with a clock. We can understand in this way how an organization endures although the separate individuals that make it up may change. Many people may laugh at this comparison. Application of a new model always seems absurd to those who use the old one. But it may be that we can find ways of controlling our ills better by speaking of ourselves as populations rather than as clocks.

This view of living organization is also of considerable help in solving the difficult problem that is left by the machine analogy, namely how living bodies are made. Machines are made by men and this was therefore at first no problem for scientists who could postulate a sort of superman in the background as Creator of the living machines. That particular use of the medieval model broke down in the nineteenth century for the same reason that medieval physics broke down in the seventeenth—because new observations were made that would not fit it. The religious system said that all plants and animals had been created as they now are, and even gave a date for the creation—4004 B.C. The studies of populations of animals and plants, past and present, showed that this could not be true and that plants, animals, and men have changed gradually to reach their present form.

Discovery of the fact of evolution came mainly from the studies of naturalists and geologists. The early scientific naturalists proceeded by the method of classification. The practice of finding likenesses, even when these are not obvious, is a characteristic activity of the human brain. These likenesses are then emphasized by the act of giving the two things a common name. The early naturalists collected, compared, classified, and, above all, named the varieties of animal and plant. By the end of the eighteenth century it was clear that quite an elaborate classification is possible. Some animals are much more alike than others, so that we can recognize sets. Cats and kangaroos are both mammals; they have fur and suckle their young. They differ in many ways from birds, but, like the latter, have backbones, as have fishes and all other vertebrates. The question arose why the Creator should have produced this sort of scheme. There was, of course, no reason why he should not have done so of his own 'will'. But another possible explanation was that there had been a gradual change; perhaps cats and kangaroos both have fur because they are descended from a common furry ancestor. Perhaps birds, mammals, and lizards all have backbones because they have descended from fishes, and so on.

This idea of evolution was not new; there had been signs of it among the Greeks. It was put forward several times in the eighteenth century, among others by Charles Darwin's own grandfather, Erasmus Darwin. But how could it be proved? The answer came from the geologists, who studied the fossils in the rocks. In the early nineteenth century it gradually became clear that the fossils are arranged in a progressive series. The layers of rock that were laid down earlier contain animals very different from those alive today. The modern types of animal appear only in the more recent strata. Finally in 1859 Darwin showed that all the degrees of difference between animals and plants can be explained by the slow divergence of the creatures. The different stages in the rocks are a series of documents proving that the process of evolution has occurred. The fact that animals and plants have changed through the millennia is more certainly proved than most of the facts of history-book history even of a few decades ago. There is no doubt that man as we now know him has existed for at the very most a few million years, and that he and the monkeys and apes are all derived by gradual divergence from a common population.

But Darwin went much farther than proving that evolution has occurred. He went on to show the connexion between the fact that the animals in the population of any one species are not all alike and their evolution. His studies of the breeding of pigeons, sheep, and other domestic animals showed him the great extent of the differences between individuals. He noticed that in every species far more are produced in each generation than can survive. This led him to the bold, if obvious, suggestion that the change we know of as evolution is due to the fact that some members of a population are more likely to survive than others. This conception has been shown by more recent studies to be essentially correct. We now realize that every population of animals and plants is very varied and is in a state of flux. The bees or the blackbirds of Scotland are rather different from those of England, just as the people are different. Evolution is going on all the time as populations gradually change.

We are thus able to make a further step in purging our language of animism. We can speak about how animals and plants have come to their present state by a continuous process that can be observed, rather than attributing their state to sudden creation by a person like ourselves. From this we can go on to discern the influences that have controlled the direction of the change. The climatic conditions in any part of the world are continually varying. We do not know very much about this variation, but there is some evidence that it goes in cycles. During the last million years there has been a series of colder periods during which the polar ice cap, which at present extends only as far as Scandinavia, has advanced, sometimes far enough to cover all Europe, and then retreated again. With such climatic changes the animals and plants resident in any region must change. As recently as 20,000 years ago there were woolly mammoths and rhinoceros and cave bears in the British Isles, which were then connected with France. Evidently the earth is not the unchanging place that it seems to the poor short experience of each of us. Once again we see how scientific study makes it impossible to maintain apparently obvious common-sense points of view.

There is, then, a continual development of new forms of life suited to the changing conditions of the environment. But when we look at the whole sequence of evolution of a large group, say the animals with vertebrae, we see something more than a series of rhythmic fluctuations following the climate. Each group of vertebrates flourishes for a while and then disappears, replaced either by its descendants or by some other animal group. Thus the fishes appeared about 350,000,000 years ago, but the present-day fishes are very different from the first ones. Then some of the fishes came out on to the land, and became amphibia. These were replaced gradually by their descendants the reptiles, until, about 70,000,000 years ago, the land and the air became peopled almost entirely with descendants of the reptiles, the mammals, and birds.

What is the meaning of this perpetual change going on in evolution? Why is it that each type of animal lasts only for a certain time and then becomes extinct? Are the new types that are continually arriving in some way higher or more efficient than the old? It is often supposed that in some sense evolution is continually progressing towards a higher type, but few have ventured to explain exactly what this means. Man is a very recent product of evolution and it is tempting to look upon the whole process as leading in his direction. This attitude we must resolutely dismiss. Many lines of evolution have nothing to do with man or with the vertebrates. We must be able to find some way of describing evolutionary change that avoids the parochialism of supposing that its end has been to produce ourselves.

The full solution of this problem begins to be visible as we realize that each life is a complicated vortex of processes, maintaining a steady state. Evolution is a change in the organization of the vortex. If we look carefully we can see that the evolutionary change involves, in many lines, a steady increase in complexity of organization. When we say that a monkey is a higher creature than a fish we do not mean only that the monkey is nearer to man. We mean that its whole way of life is more complicated, that it has more parts, and that it does more things. Now the things that an animal does are its means of getting a living from its environment. So if it does more things that must mean that it has to work harder to get its living. This is exactly what I believe we shall find that the higher animals do. They live in surroundings that are less suitable for life than those of the lower animals and therefore they have to do more work for their living. To put it in another way, the higher creatures show greater differences from their surroundings than do the lower ones. As a physicist would put it, the higher are less probable, less random, systems.

This brings us back directly to the central theme of these lectures, the nature of the action of the brain and the alternation of doubt and certainty. The changes in evolution occur by natural selection of the differences among the members of populations. These differences are produced by the processes of mutation or random change of hereditary factors and the random shuffling of these factors by sexual reproduction. Looking at the long course of evolution it seems that by the process of variation and selection populations have been produced that are able to support life under continually more and more difficult conditions. There is a certain parallel between this finding of new environments by evolution and by the formation of new associations in the brain. In the brain, by association and learning, things that were not previously significant for life are made to become so. The whole history of social man has been the continual discovery by random trial and error of new tools, technical and verbal, that enable life to be lived in ways not possible before. Man, in pursuing this alternate process of doubting and then applying the rules that he learns, is carrying on the plan that evolution has always been pursuing. It is sometimes lamented that science seems to take us continually farther and farther from nature, that is to say it makes life possible by more and more elaborate devices. But this is just what animals and plants have been doing for 1,000,000,000 years or more. The biologists' method of description has certainly much to commend it if it shows us how the learning process in our brains is part of a development that has been going on ever since life began.

Comment on the Seventh Lecture

I T would obviously be possible to amplify this lecture greatly by further discussion of the words that man has used to describe himself and other living things. Sir Charles Sherrington has added to the great debt we owe to him in other ways by giving us a careful examination of the system of medicine used in the sixteenth century, as shown in the work of the French physician Jean Fernel. Medical language was then, as now, linked with the common language system of the age. For us the natural way of speaking about a body is as something that has 'structure' and 'functions', like a machine. In the sixteenth century few would have understood such talk at all. The human body, like all earthly things, was then said to be composed of the four elements, earth, air, fire, and water. Each of these contributed to the temperament of the individual, giving the 'qualities' of dryness, wetness, warmth, and cold. Disease was due to an upset of the balance of qualities natural to the individual. The qualities were represented in the body by the four humours. Black bile or melancholy humour was stored in the spleen and was equivalent to earth. The blood was the equivalent to air and the yellow bile or choler of the liver to fire. The phlegm or pituita of the nose, supposed to be secreted by the brain, was the human equivalent to water.

To describe the way the substance of the body was produced this early physiology made an analogy with cooking. The three coctions served to convert the food into the substance of the body. The first coction, in the stomach, converted the food into chyle, the contents of the stomach. In the second coction, in the liver, this was converted into blood and in the third coction the flesh was made from the blood. The mind or anima was in this system much more widely dispersed through the body than in our modern thinking. Each part of the body was supposed to have its own special faculty or part of the mind. Thus each part possessed the power of having feelings, for instance of pleasure in attracting particular components of the blood to itself. The whole system thus interpreted the changes that go on in the body as though each one was produced by a little person who had attributes like our own. The gall-bladder, Fernel says, has an affinity with the yellow bile, and experiences satisfaction and pleasure in attracting the latter. Let us take warning from the way in which the system of Fernel, only 400 years old, now seems to us crude and absurd. It may be that our own will not seem so very much better even 100 years hence.

Medical terminology was linked with the physics of the time through the science of astrology. The motions of the celestial spheres that controlled the planets and other heavenly bodies also controlled human lives. Part of the business of the physician in making his diagnosis was therefore to discover these connexions, so that he might best forecast the course of the patient's health and the treatment to be adopted. Fernel was brought up to believe in astrology, but he abandoned it when his own observations failed to find it useful. Here we see the beginning in medicine of the system of independent inquiry and observation, replacing strict attention to authority. It is no coincidence that it was Fernel who introduced the term Physiology, as the sub-title for the second edition of his *Natural Part of Medicine*, issued in 1554.

But he still continued to use in the main the old terminology, and it was not until the next century that comparison with man-made machines began seriously to invade biological science, for example in Descartes' attempt to compare the workings of the nervous system with those of a clock. This comparison was only partially successful and Descartes himself made only few biological observations. A better example of the rise of the mechanistic method was the discovery of the circulation of the blood by William Harvey, physician to Charles I. Harvey's account was published in 1628, but he had lectured about it at least thirteen years earlier. He was able to show that a whole series of facts fits together on the assumption that the heart is a pump sending blood into the arteries, from which it returns into veins. To us the idea seems obvious—why was it not discovered before? One can compare the heart with a pump only when pumps have been invented, but of course that had been done much earlier and the comparison was not new. The trouble was that the arteries as seen with even the best dissection do not seem to join the veins. Anatomists at the time agreed about this and concluded that since both arteries and veins end blindly it must be that the heart pumps the blood backwards and forwards along each of them.

But Harvey did just what doubters always do, he noticed a lot of things that could only be explained on the assumption that, contrary to all apparent sense, the blood *does* circulate. He went on to consider the consequences of this rule, for example, in the way the blood is held back by the valves that can be seen by everyone in the veins of the arm. He made further experiments and they all agreed with this view. So he announced that there must be very fine connecting tubes between the arteries and veins, although they could not be seen. Thirty-two years later, when microscopes had been perfected, Malpighi was able to see the blood actually flowing through these fine tubes, the capillaries. As a footnote it may be mentioned that we now know that the tube idea is only partly right—the walls of the capillaries are very peculiar leaky tubes, not impervious like ordinary waterpipes, and they are continually letting out a lot of the watery part of the blood, which flows around the cells and is then sucked back into the veins. Harvey, like everyone else, was only partly right; there are always further new observations to be made.

Study of living processes by the physiological method only proceeded laboriously behind the study of non-living systems. Knowledge about respiration, for instance, began to become well organized as the study of combustion proceeded, since this is an analogous operation. Indeed Lavoisier at the end of the eighteenth century performed experiments upon oxygen equally as consumed by flames and by animals. It was only as chemistry expanded during the nineteenth century that really powerful models for living activities became available.

However, the more we come to know of the flux of chemical changes in the body the more one great weakness of the machine analogy stands out. The concept of a dynamic organization, such as that of a whirlpool, demands a consideration of time—of before and after and of the gradual development and change of pattern, but the machine models of physiology allow no place for this element. A man-made machine is built by us and there it stands ready for use. If we are to go farther we have to find a model or models that will help us to answer not only questions like 'What is it?', meaning 'What is it made of?', but also 'How does it come to be as it is?' This is the place that the study of heredity, embryology, and evolution plays in the whole picture. Physiologists and biochemists have paid and still pay rather little attention to these subjects. They have often used embryos and animals other than man for experiments, but they have left the study of evolution to others, they have not found ways of describing how the organization of the body comes to be as it is. There were indeed at first no methods by which organization could be studied at all. Physiology began by making its comparisons with machines, which do not evolve except when we change them. What we need is some understanding of the way in which the design of living things comes to be changed. That is what is not allowed for in any scheme that only compares living things with man-made machines. The question hardly arose in the seventeenth and eighteenth centuries and men did not see any connexions that allowed them to get beyond the primitive stage of saying that living machines were created as they are by god. They went on using the old model of the world as something made by a god resembling man. To complete our view of modern science we have therefore to see how it came about that man was able to dispense with that childish model of creation and to see a little farther into the grand scheme by which things have come to appear as they do today.

This was of course achieved by the discovery that animal and plant organization gradually changes, and that it is enabled to do so because of the differences between the members of each species. The study of variation presents certain special difficulties because it involves the opposite of our basic tendency to compare things, to find likenesses and to give names. The point of examining all the variety of individuals in a population, say of men, is to show the respects in which they are *not* alike. This is an activity that is difficult and distasteful for the type of brain that looks for the easy and obvious solutions achieved by classification. For many people the only satisfactory way of speaking about the world is in terms of a series of sharply defined categories, the properties of which are exactly known. Such a procedure has great advantages, but it severely limits our powers of speaking about all the variety that we observe around us. In order to include this variety it has been necessary to invent a special statistical mathematics. This enables us to compare not only the average size of, say, the people of England and Italy but also the extent of the deviations from the average that are present in each case. With this instrument it been possible to proceed with the study of variation and to show how necessary variety is for the maintenance of the continuity of each race. Only where there is sufficient variety is it ensured that there are always individuals available with characteristics suitable to meet the changes that occur in the climate and other features of the environment.

An interesting feature of the study of variation and evolution is that it has taken a considerable time for it to begin to give results of practical value to mankind. Of course the study of the improvement of man's animals and crops by breeding has been a preoccupation of the agriculturalist for ages; but the matter is so complicated that it has been very difficult to discover the principles by which it may be treated. The decisive step was of course the discovery by Mendel in 1866 of the fact that individual characteristics may be inherited in certain fixed proportions. To give a recent example, a type of white mouse appeared by mutation among black mice exposed to X-rays. When this was mated with a black mouse the offspring were all grey. If two of these greys were then mated together the next generation contained blacks, whites, and greys in the proportion of 1 : 1 : 2. This is explained by assuming that each of the original mice carried a pair of genes or hereditary factors for black or white on their chromosomes. Each of the offspring therefore inherits one black and one white gene and the result is grey. Each egg and sperm produced by these greys will carry *either* the black *or* the white gene, and there are so many sperms that the chances of each egg being fertilized by a sperm carrying black or white are equal. Thus although the geneticist cannot forecast the colour of any one mouse, he can say that on the average the three types will be present in the second generation in proportions of 1:1:2.

By means of very laborious studies geneticists have now established that there are thousands of pairs of genes in each individual, carried on the pairs of chromosomes that occupy the nucleus of each cell. The genes usually stay the same from generation to generation, but in about one in every half-million generations each gene changes and produces a new type. The variety of organisms in a population is the result partly of these changes known as mutations and partly of the reshuffling of the chromosomes that goes on in each generation, through the process of sexual reproduction from two parents.

Since there are so many genes in each individual, forecasting and controlling the characteristics is a very complicated business, and it has taken more than fifty years before these discoveries have become really fruitful. Even now we cannot control animal and plant organization as we should wish and some people in Russia and elsewhere have become impatient and have condemned this whole science of genetics as sterile and reactionary. Impatience for results is understandable and indeed in a sense correct. Science and its words are in the end practical, they serve to ensure that so many of us can live on the earth. Why is it that scientists feel sure that the geneticists have been right in pursuing their careful experiments on the inheritance of hundreds of features of the little fly *Drosophila*? The theories that resulted did not seem to help us to produce better wheat. The famous wheats that resist the rust diseases were bred mainly without these theories, by the simple method of choosing the plants that did not get the diseases.

The geneticists went on with their work because they found that each discovery led to another one and they could not feel that this way of talking about our experience was sterile if it kept on leading to new observation. And now as practical men we can begin to see that they were right. The geneticists have given us a way of talking and thinking about inheritance that is going to be of great value in getting us out of the awkward situation that the practical plant and animal breeders have produced. The better wheats and fruits and potatoes that the breeders have created give of course much better yields than the mixed stocks that agriculturists used before. They may resist disease better too, but there is a difficulty, as there always is in any system of ideas that suggests that all that is necessary is to find the best and then cling to it. This seems to be a very natural way of thinking, but it is a fatal one in the end—for all life changes and even the apparently best way of looking at it will not last for ever. It is a paradox that the only way in which one can be sure of continuance is to be ready for change. In the case of the crops the trouble is that the various parasites and pests that attack them do not remain unchanged. The new plants may be resistant to 999 of the bacteria or aphids, but the thousandth will be a different one which can manage to carry on. From it a new race of parasites will emerge to which our precious new plant is *not* immune. In fact this new race of pests will be able to have a specially good time because we have obligingly planted enormous numbers of nearly identical plants for it to consume, instead of the various ones that are present in most populations: it will soon eat its way through them all.

Doctors Darlington and Mather, who have dealt with these matters recently, have shown how by using the theories of modern genetics we can meet this situation and build up stocks that have the good characteristics and yet are varied and therefore able to meet the challenge of new enemies. This not only emphasizes the value of variety but also shows the reward for all the efforts of the geneticists. If the yield of wheat per acre is increased by even a tenth part by genetics, then we have a tool that can help the human population enormously.

The study of genetics and of evolution has greatly improved our power of speaking about living things and controlling them. Indeed this improvement is still going on rapidly at the present time. We are beginning to learn how to combine our knowledge of biochemistry and physiology with that of genetics, producing a new science of Chemical Embryology, to use the title of Dr. Joseph Needham's great book on the subject. We are getting beyond the early stage in which the genes were regarded simply as mysterious entities that reside in the chromosomes and control the course of development from the egg so as to make offspring like their parents. We now know a little of the chemical nature of the chromosomes, and of the peculiar nucleo-proteins that they contain. The pattern of activity of these substances is ultimately responsible for the control of all the activities within the cells, not only while the embryo is developing but also throughout life. There is reason to think that as we come to know more about these substances and the patterns of their action we shall acquire a much fuller understanding and control of the whole life of ourselves and other organisms. Many of our major ills are defects of the working of our pattern of organization—cancer, for example, is due to the excessive growth of cells that have for some reason changed from their normal orderly behaviour. The control of this and many other conditions becomes more nearly a possibility as we pass on from the comparison of the body with simple machines, which has been the basis of physiology and medicine in the past. As we come to speak about our organization more freely we gradually improve the methods by which it can be controlled. I have mentioned already the possibilities of understanding any organization by comparison with human populations. Perhaps a still more hopeful terminology is to compare the process of inheritance with the operation of machines that transmit information. Dr. Kalmus has suggested that we can consider the genes as carrying information from one generation to the next. Thus we get the possibility of using the whole apparatus of mathematics that describes the transmission of information for analysing how the workings of the body for every moment of its life are controlled by the information it has received from the millions of generations in the past.

Eighth Lecture

MADE IN WHAT IMAGE?

THESE lectures have tried to show that it is a great advantage to talk about ourselves by describing what goes on in our brains. However, this is still a rather unfamiliar way of speaking; it is not easy to use yet because we have not had much practice with it and we have not enough detailed facts about how the brain works. I have tried in the time to give an idea of the different sorts of information that are available and to show what we can do with them. We can talk conveniently about many of the more interesting things that men do by speaking of the rules that become established in their brains. Admittedly we know as yet only very little about these rules, and one aim of these lectures has been to show how much we might be able to do if we took the trouble to find out more. This study of the brain is certainly one of the most challenging of all scientific problems. At present we spend much of our mathematical and physical genius on study of the world around us. Why not apply more of it to ourselves and especially to our brains?

The very idea may seem absurd to many scientists. That is because the poverty of our current language about the brain gives little hint of the richness of the problems to be solved. In order to show that this poverty might be overcome I have tried to speak about even the most complicated human behaviour in terms of the actions of the brain cells. To give at least a primitive way of talking about these actions we have considered that the brain has rules that sort out the input coming from the sense organs. The rules act, as we might say, as models, as standards of comparison. Speaking of rules and of models must be at best only a crude way of presenting the nature of brain action. The point is that we need some way that will stimulate us to make investigations and to find out more.

One of the results that has emerged is that use of our knowledge about the brain alters considerably the way we speak about ourselves. In the seventh lecture it was suggested that the practice has been growing up of using, for this purpose, a new basic standard model. We are getting the habit of speaking more and more about populations, with all their variety. The use of this model alters the way we speak about many things, including our own selves, and it provides a new system that unifies many fields of activity, from physics, through biology, to sociology. In fact, it is not too much to say that it is the basic model for the functioning of modern societies.

Each human society usually has some central model as the canon of its system, a symbol that provides, if you like, something that everyone agrees is important, so that conversation and writing can proceed. In the Middle Ages the symbols of religion provided such a model; statements were 'true' if they abounded to the glory of God. Then, as time went on, men adopted various other ways of speaking and found that they could say more. The central model or reference point now became the individual person. Descartes might be said to have founded modern philosophy and habits of language with his famous 'I think, therefore I am'. The new basic unit that we have used has been what we might call the experiencing I or ego. We cast all our speech into the form that it takes place between two units, you and I. We picture, as the physicists put it, a world of observers. The basic canon of the system is that it deals with verifiable observation. Probably most scientists would say that a true statement is one that can potentially be verified by anyone who takes the trouble to learn the necessary skill.

This is where the biologist steps in, for his business is the description of living organisms, such as these observers— the physicists. He insists that he finds that they are not all alike. They differ, for example, in their brains and the rules that are in them. It is not adequate, therefore, to define truth as that which can be observed and verified by anyone. The biologist goes on to suggest that we are mistaken in this emphasis on individual observers. They are not the basic units of life. Each individual is part of a much larger system, which continues over millions of years, changing slowly by the process of evolution. This maintenance of continuity is the most fundamental feature that the biologist can see, and he suggests that all human action should be spoken about relative to it.

This way of speaking in terms of continuity means changing a good deal our apparatus of words. In any system of language the basic fact is that of communication—the transfer of information. This certainly presupposes agents, persons, egos, whatever you like, that do the interchanging. But our way of speaking has magnified these egos to such an extent as to obscure the reason for which we originally postulated them, namely to speak about their communication. We learn very early in life to talk like this about ourselves, so that it becomes the obvious thing to do. It may seem absurd to doubt the primacy of oneself; probably most of us tend to say, 'One must begin somewhere and the one thing I cannot doubt is the existence of myself and my experience'. But biology has shown us to what an extraordinary extent our ways of observing and speaking are not our own, but, like our whole organization, are inherited and learned. We are in fact already coming to speak of ourselves in quite a different way—not as one thing but as a great variety of them. Marcel Proust expresses this when, speaking of his own personality, he says, 'I was not one man only, but the steady parade hour after hour of an army in close formation, in which there appeared, according to the moment, impassioned men, indifferent men, jealous men— jealous men no two of whom were jealous of the same woman.'

Is this another way of describing the situation that I have expressed by saying that modern man has learned to use in his brain a whole variety of models? In the Middle Ages all talk was unified around one central set of symbols and this made for great compactness in society. After that time men broke away from this way of speaking and their brains became filled with a number of lesser rules, of models of machines, and so on, each suitable for conveying some sorts of information. But we have continued up to now to use the old sorts of speech in describing ourselves. We each probably still say, if pressed, something like, 'The central thing that I know is my mind, my experience, my consciousness.' That is to say we refer to ourselves as if we were a body occupied by a person—the old model of a circle with something inside it. Is it possible that we should convey more information if we tried to do without this whole apparatus of the words of conventional psychology? We can say everything that we want to say quite well without speaking all the time as if we were inhabited by this spirit called the mind.

One of the principles of science since the seventeenth century has been to try to speak only of that which was observable—to be direct. In a sense the extraordinary discoveries of relativity flow from directness of description. We must not say that a rod has such-and-such a length, but must describe exactly what we have done to measure it. We must not interpose the 'occult quality', as Newton might have called it, of length into our description. May it be that the terminology of psychology consists of a series of occult qualities interposed in this way? They are models, if you like, used for convenience of description; we can do without them when we get better ones. Take the case of consciousness. In order to talk we postulate this entity as a kind of something within ourselves. 'But how can I doubt', you may say, 'that I have something called consciousness? I have consciousness and I may lose it when I bang my head.' But what is it that you really mean to say—that you lose it in the sense you lose a penny when it rolls under the sideboard? Of course not—what you meant to say was that following some particular blow on the back of your head you were unable to act as an observer or transmitter for ten minutes. 'Of course', you may reply, 'you can put it like that if you wish and I agree it tells you a little more detail, but what else is gained by your new method? Is it not much easier and less clumsy to say "I lost consciousness"?' Surely the danger is that if we use these old methods we shall be misled into all the fallacies that would follow if we supposed consciousness to be a single thing, which could exist independently of the rest of ourselves. If it is a thing in the ordinary sense it could be observed directly like any object. No one claims to be able to observe consciousness in that way. We may, there-fore, be pretty sure that it is one of these occult qualities.

Let us try to describe ourselves exactly to each other. We shall find that we can do better than by trying to speak of ourselves as inhabited by a number of pseudo-things such as consciousness, mind, experience, and the rest of them. Of course, this is making the situation out at its worst. Few people speak of the mind as if it were a simple thing. It is a truism that our powers are compounded from many sources. The suggestion is that we should now fully recognize this, face the multiplicity of ourselves and speak less as if we were inhabited by a semi-thing—the mind.

We now have enough facts to enable us to picture quite fully the inheritance of our system from our parents. We can follow how, by education, elaborate rules of action grow up in our brains. We each come to possess, as we might say, a whole population of models. Some of us have more, some less, according to our abilities and experience. What we now have to do is to try to put all this information together to give a new model of ourselves. I suggest that we can do it if we can imagine the way the cells of our brains are arranged and organized. This organization is so vast that to speak adequately about it we must compare it with the action of a very large population, say that of the whole human race. We have to try to find ways of speaking about all the group-ings and actions and conflicts of the hundreds of millions of cells in the brain. Only when study has proceeded much farther shall we acquire a really satisfactory picture of our-selves in this way, as part of a continuous organization. Probably we shall need for this an elaborate statistical and mathematical terminology. But already we can see that it provides a better way of speaking, for many purposes, than is obtained by emphasis on a compact entity, the individual ego. Some such way of speaking can do much to unify the separate parts of science. It is an idiom that arises naturally out of the recent developments of a number of branches of science, such as behaviourist psychology, physics, and socio-logy. It arises from the biologist's thesis that from the study of the evolution of living things we acquire a new model or standard with which to make comparisons.

The early scientists organized their talk by finding 'laws', that is to say by comparison with human society. They also compared the universe and the human body with machines—that is to say with our tools. Now we are learning to speak by comparison with human and animal populations, which present the widest expression of continuity that we know. What will be the results of this change? There are already distinct signs that in future there will be less sharp separa-tion between physical, biological, and sociological science than there is now. All of these sciences report the behaviour of the same populations of observers. Their business is to describe these in all their variety, and particularly the variety of brains and their rules. The aim of the new unified science might be said to be to define those relations between popula-tions of people that enable them to communicate informa-tion and so to maintain life. This is the way of speaking that can unify all our scientific activities. That, of course, does not mean that we may not be able to doubt it in the future; one may expect that further and better models will be developed, just as this one is now arising out of previous systems.

If this evolutionary model is so powerful it should be of practical value. Speaking by comparison is useful to man-kind because it enables us to make better tools and thus aids survival; the point of the talking is to work together and to plan. The better our words and other symbols become, the better we can live. By using each of the special sorts of scientific language we can make useful plans to help mankind—for example in building houses, making chemicals, or breeding better wheat. It is often complained that while we have all these separate scientific skills yet we lack a general scheme for mankind as a whole. Evolutionary theory provides that general plan. It comprehends within itself all the other sciences, providing a general science that compounds the activities of all the others and enables us to make useful forecasts and plans for large human groups or the whole of society. This may sound grandiose, perhaps even absurd, but it is said soberly. Studies of populations and their evolution are useful because they show us how to talk about and plan all our varied affairs. It is presumably no accident that the century that has seen the growth of evolutionary biology has also produced the science of sociology, with all its implications.

The picture could be made more specific by suggesting changes that the new ways of speaking may produce in fields as wide apart as technology, metaphysics, ethics, and politics. No doubt there will be development of many sorts of tools at present used in engineering, industry, and agriculture. But the special contribution of the new model will be to keep in perspective at all times the relative position of men and the tools that they use. There is already a pronounced tendency to do this. The old plan was to make the machine first and then to sit the man uncomfortably in it. Now the human operator is studied at every stage. We make the machine to fit him, and study how to teach him to use the machine. Above all we learn where to find the weak links in the maintenance of the whole system. All such work is made easier by the development of tools of communication. More and more these tools are coming to depend not only on physical research, as our past machines have done, but are the product largely of investigation of ourselves and especially of our brains.

The new machines will probably be mainly electrical and will be such as to ensure much more nearly direct communication between brains than is possible now. It may be that by scanning the electrical activities in the head we shall read each other's brains. This is not so revolutionary as it sounds. Throughout broadcast lectures the listeners almost scan the lecturer's brain with their electrical equipment. Electrical devices have made it possible for one to speak to many, and the one person's brain works very hard to find symbols that will match those in so many brains. Improvement in communication therefore leads to increasing accuracy, directness, and completeness of description. These are tendencies that are evident in many fields of language and literature today.

Future methods of observation and communication will enable people to be better orientated in relation to their place in the universe than in the past. They will have a much better understanding of themselves and their relationship to the continuity of life that is our fundamental experience. Exactly how that continuity and communication may be symbolized I do not venture to forecast. No doubt old symbols will be used to a large extent: all these changes are but developments of what has gone on before. No doubt as we apply the new tools we shall gradually come to know much more of the universe and our place in it. Some of the revelations that will be provided may be strange. In the past we have continued to rely for our general views essentially on the medieval conception that the universe was created at some finite time in the past. But do we need to consider that the universe started at all? This may seem absurd until you realize how limited and arbitrary is our present view that there was a beginning. It is an unwarranted extension. When two people walk off in opposite directions it seems that they will never meet. And yet we now know that the earth is round. One of our hardest lessons is to learn that apparently obvious extensions of the use of our rules may lead us astray. We must balance certainty by doubt. In this case our short experience of time and existence does not warrant us in postulating any creation or beginning at all. To do so is our crude way of talking about things, in terms of the model that speaks of the basic reality of life as an I, with a beginning and an end. Biological discovery has shown that this assumption of a sudden beginning for each of us is not true. Our organization, the most essential and enduring thing about us, does not begin from nothing, but is passed on continually. Perhaps we make our world picture with a beginning and an end because we have conceived too narrowly of our own beginnings and ends. If we could only look farther behind and ahead we might see a different picture.

Perhaps instead of focusing on beginning as the act of creation we should do exactly the opposite and centre our speech on continuity. The sense in which we do see creation is in the building of organization that goes on in the life of each individual, especially, in the case of man, in our brains. Each individual thus forms his own way of life, his own order and rules, and these are valuable to the race because each is unique. Certainly our rules are largely acquired, but it is because individuals are *not* all alike that our kind is so adaptable and maintains its dominance. Each individual uses the store of randomness with which he is born to build, during his life, rules that are useful and can be passed on.

Similarly we can detect in the progress of evolution a decrease in randomness of all living things. The higher animals are in a sense more different from their surroundings than are the lower. We might therefore take as our general picture of the universe a system of continuity in which there are two elements—randomness and organization—disorder and order if you like, alternating with each other in such a fashion as to maintain continuity. Is it possible that the data of the astronomers can also be interpreted as showing the universe as a system of balancing, of maintaining a steady state, just as our living system does, with the characteristic that it builds up systems of order and then returns them to disorder? You may say that this is very crude anthropomorphism. Certainly it is, but no more crude than that of imagining a creation. Astronomical evidence tells us all sorts of things about how some stars heat up while others cool. New hydrogen appears and forms into more complex elements. Stars and galaxies are built out of the disorder, then recede away, perhaps into randomness.

The picture is not complete or satisfactory, but it seems to show at least signs of a correspondence and unity between organic and astronomical happenings. Perhaps we might say that if all this is correct there appear to us to be two general laws of the universe: first, that of association, of binding, the tendency for randomly distributed processes to become linked together to form larger units; second is the law that such unity is not permanent, but sooner or later dissolves, providing fresh randomness. This certainly seems to be a general principle in biology and we have seen how it usefully describes the progress of the growth of our brains and of the whole organization of our species, by alternation of aggregation and disaggregation. Each species remains in balance with its surroundings by alternate periods of development and death, followed by replacement by a new version of the organization. This is the means by which life maintains, as it were, communication with the non-living world. It is perhaps not fantastic to say that a corresponding method of communication prevails throughout the universe. There is a rhythmic building by alternation of organization and disorder, a continuous process of 'creation'.

The wide vision we have acquired by our new systems of language and tools enables us to see continuity extending a considerable way into the past. We can follow in outline the whole evolution of life from simple organisms, more than 1,000,000,000 years ago. We cannot yet say for certain how life first arose, but we can imagine that it happened gradually, as a result of conditions obtaining at that time. We still do not know exactly how our earth took the form we now see, but the date seems to have been about 3,000,000,000 years ago or rather more. We can try to follow continuity still farther backwards and to see our whole position in the universe. But here we find ourselves more baffled: we cannot properly comprehend the pattern of the stars. Our astronomers are working hard to find rules of brain action that shall make us able to do so, but in spite of their considerable discoveries I feel sure that they would agree that they have not yet found the really significant clue. In this respect we are all like the people born blind, who on receiving their sight see only a revolving mass of lights. It is not to belittle the conclusions of astronomers to say that when we look at the heavens we are as babies—we have no means of understanding the significance of what we see. It is exciting to speculate that one day we may comprehend more fully the frame in which we are set.

Until we can understand the stars we shall probably be wise to continue to base our actions upon the stability of life upon the earth. By an adequate supply of variation life has managed to remain continuous for at least 1,000,000,000 years. Mammalian organization was well established long before the Himalayas or the Alps took their present form. We shall not go far wrong if we base our talk and actions upon this continuity of life, which is certainly as stable as any other basis we can see. We need some such canon for establishing our rules, and deciding the principles of education by which these rules are taught. There are some reasons for believing that this continuity will be the central model or rule of our brains, at least for the immediate future.

Many of these considerations are of course tentative. I am not sure how far they are the result of excessive preoccupation throughout these lectures with the subject of communication. They are, indeed, the logical outcome of that preoccupation. My whole thesis is that our thoughts can conveniently be organized by focusing our attention on the importance of communication and the way that it is ensured by the brain. At best what we are producing is a system of the universe as conceived by man, the talking animal. Our brains work like this and we cannot help it. But I should like to emphasize that to communicate is not our whole nature. It is our means of getting a living as a social animal, but it is only a means, not living itself. One great mistake of modern man is to worry too much about his means of living —his models and his comparisons. We must go on making them and we can greatly enjoy doing so. They are a chief glory in our way of life, but they are not the whole of life. A fine morning, a good meal, work well done and a pleasant sleep, these are as truly our life as is talking about them. We can enjoy life and, like the birds, we must sing about it. The octopus and the plants and the sky and the stars do not sing or talk, but are not the less real for that.

It is of our very nature to see the universe as a place that we can talk about. In particular, you will remember, the brain tends to compute by organizing all of its input into certain *general* patterns. It is natural for us, therefore, to try to make these grand abstractions, to seek for one formula, one model, one God, around which we can organize all our communication and the whole business of living.

REFERENCES

ADRIAN, E. D. (1947). *The Physical Background of Perception*. Oxford, Clarendon Press.

AYER, A. J. (1947). *Thinking and Meaning*. Inaugural lecture. London: H. K. Lewis.

—— (1948). *Language, Truth and Logic*. London: Gollancz.

CRAIK, K. J. W. (1943). *The Nature of Explanation*. Cambridge University Press.

CREED, R. S., *et al*. (1932). *Reflex Activity of the Spinal Cord*. Oxford, Clarendon Press.

DARLINGTON, C. D., and MATHER, K. (1950). *Genes, Plants and People*. London: Allen and Unwin.

DINGLE, H. (1941). 'The Foundations of Empirical Knowledge.' *Nature*, **147**, 286.

—— (1949). 'The Nature of Scientific Philosophy.' *Proc. Roy. Soc. Edinburgh*, **62**, 400.

—— (1949). 'Scientific and Philosophical Implications of the Special Theory of Relativity.' *Library of Living Philosophers*, **7**: Albert Einstein, Philosopher Scientist.

EVANS-PRITCHARD, E. E. (1940). *The Nuer*. Oxford, Clarendon Press.

FARRELL, B. A. (1950). 'Experience.' *Mind*, N.S. **59**, 170.

FORDE, C. D. (1934). *Habitat, Economy and Society*. London: Methuen.

FULTON, J. F. (1949). *Physiology of the Nervous System*. 3rd ed. New York: Oxford University Press.

HALDANE, J. B. S. (1932). *The Causes of Evolution*. London: Longmans, Green.

—— (1941). *New Paths in Genetics*. London: Allen and Unwin.

HARVEY, W. (1628). *An Anatomical Disquisition on the Motion of the Heart and Blood in Animals*. (Everyman's Library.) London: Dent.

HEBB, D. O. (1949). *The Organisation of Behaviour*. London: Chapman and Hall; New York: John Wiley.

HOGBEN, L. T. (1940). *Science for the Citizen*. 2nd ed. London: Allen and Unwin.

JAMES, W. (1950). *Biography* by Margaret Knight. Penguin Books, Pelican Series, Harmondsworth Press.

KÖHLER, W. (1925). *The Mentality of Apes*. London: Kegan Paul.

LASHLEY, K. S. (1929). 'Brain Mechanisms and Intelligence.' *Brain Research Fund Monographs*, I. Chicago University Press.

—— (1948). 'The Mechanism of Vision.' *Genetic Psychology Monographs*, **37**, 107.

MUMFORD, L. (1934). *Technics and Civilization*. London: Routledge.

NEEDHAM, J. (1928). *Man a Machine*. New York: W. W. Norton.

—— (1931). *Chemical Embryology*. 3 vols. Cambridge University Press.

NEWTON, SIR ISAAC. (1946). *Newton Tercentenary Celebrations*. The Royal Society. Andrade, E. N. da C., 'Newton', p. 3; Keynes, Lord, 'Newton, the Man', p. 35; Vavilov, S. I., 'Newton and the Atomic Theory', p. 43. Cambridge University Press, 1947.

PENFIELD, W., and RASMUSSEN, T. (1950). *The Cerebral Cortex of Man*. New York: MacMillan.

RYLE, G. (1949). *The Concept of Mind*. London: Hutchinson.

SCHRÖDINGER, E. (1944). *What is Life? The Physical Aspect of the Living Cell*. Cambridge University Press.

SHERRINGTON, SIR CHARLES. (1906). *The Integrative Action of the Nervous System*. London: Constable.

——— (1946). *The Endeavour of Jean Fernel*. Cambridge University Press.

SIMPSON, G. G. (1950). *The Meaning of Evolution*. London: Oxford University Press.

THE PHYSICAL BASIS OF MIND (1950). Broadcast Talks. Contributions by C. S. Sherrington, E. D. Adrian, A. J. Ayer, W. R. Brain, W. E. Le Gros Clark, W. Penfield, Lord Samuel, S. Zuckerman, G. Ryle, E. T. O. Slater.

THOMPSON, SIR D'A. W. (1942). *Essays on Growth and Form*. Cambridge University Press.

WHITEHEAD, A. N. (1926). *Science and the Modern World*. Cambridge University Press.

WIENER, N. (1949). *Cybernetics*. New York: John Wiley.

INDEX

PRINTED IN GREAT BRITAIN
AT THE UNIVERSITY PRESS, OXFORD
BY CHARLES BATEY, PRINTER TO THE UNIVERSITY